creating
character
ARCS
WORKBOOK

creating character ARCS WORKBOOK

PEN FOR A SWORD

"If you did your job as a writer, you know that your central character will be changed, your reader will be changed, and so will you."
—John Dufresne

Also by K.M. Weiland:

A Man Called Outlaw

Behold the Dawn

Dreamlander

Storming

Digital Shorts
The Memory Lights

One More Ride in the Rain

The Saddle Daddy Rode

Non-Fiction
Creating Character Arcs

Outlining Your Novel

Outlining Your Novel Workbook

Structuring Your Novel

Structuring Your Novel Workbook

Jane Eyre: The Writer's Digest Annotated Classic

Conquering Writer's Block and Summoning Inspiration

5 Secrets of Story Struvture

TABLE OF CONTENTS

Introduction..11

Choose Which Character Arc You Will Use............................15

Chapter One: The Positive Change Arc.............................**19**

The Lie Your Character Believes..................................21

Symptoms of the Lie...25

The Thing Your Character Needs................................29

The Thing Your Character Wants................................33

Your Character's Ghost...37

The Characteristic Moment..41

The Normal World...48

The First Act..55

The First Plot Point...61

The First Half of the Second Act................................66

The Midpoint...70

The Second Half of the Second Act...........................74

The Third Plot Point...80

The First Half of the Third Act...................................84

The Climax..89

The Resolution...93

Chapter Two: The Flat Arc...**97**

The Truth Your Character Believes.............................99

The Normal World...102

The Characteristic Moment..106

The First Act..112

The First Plot Point...117

The First Half of the Second Act................................121

The Midpoint...124

The Second Half of the Second Act...........................127

The Third Plot Point...131

The First Half of the Third Act...................................135

The Climax..138

The Resolution...141

Chapter Three: The Negative Change Arc #1: Disillusionment....................**145**

    The Lie Your Character Believes....................147

    The Thing Your Character Needs....................150

    The Thing Your Character Wants....................153

    The Characteristic Moment....................156

    The Normal World....................163

    The First Act....................167

    The First Plot Point....................173

    The First Half of the Second Act....................177

    The Midpoint....................181

    The Second Half of the Second Act....................185

    The Third Plot Point....................190

    The First Half of the Third Act....................193

    The Climax....................198

    The Resolution....................200

Chapter Four: The Negative Change Arc #2: Fall....................**205**

    The Lie Your Character Believes....................207

    Symptoms of the Lie....................210

    Your Character's Ghost....................213

    The Thing Your Character Needs....................216

    The Thing Your Character Wants....................219

    The Characteristic Moment....................223

    The Normal World....................230

    The First Act....................233

    The First Plot Point....................239

    The First Half of the Second Act....................243

    The Midpoint....................247

    The Second Half of the Second Act....................250

    The Third Plot Point....................255

    The First Half of the Third Act....................258

    The Climax....................262

    The Resolution....................266

Chapter Five: The Negative Change Arc #3: Corruption....................**271**

    The Truth Your Character Believes....................273

    Your Character's Ghost....................275

The Thing Your Character Wants...279

The Normal World...282

The Characteristic Moment..285

The First Act...293

The First Plot Point..297

The First Half of the Second Act..301

The Midpoint..305

The Second Half of the Second Act..308

The Third Plot Point...313

The First Half of the Third Act..316

The Climax...319

The Resolution..323

Conclusion..**327**

INTRODUCTION

WRITING A GREAT character, in itself, isn't enough to create a great story. If you're going to write a story worthy of that amazing character, the first thing you have to do is learn how to write character *arcs* that resonate with your readers and leave them gasping, cheering, or crying. Or all three.

As I discuss in my book *Creating Character Arcs*, "How to write character arcs?" isn't just any old question for a writer. It's one of *the* questions. Master the tenets of Positive Change Arcs, Flat Arcs, and Negative Change Arcs, and you'll be able to write any story with confidence and skill.

Figuring out how to write character arcs takes your understanding of story far beyond that of just a character changing over the course the story. It will take you beyond even the all-important foundation of story structure to the core principles of story theory (which I've already talked about, in depth, in *Structuring Your Novel* and the *Structuring Your Novel Workbook*).

Character evolution is at the heart of any good story. Whether it's the protagonist doing the changing, or whether he's changing the world around him, character arcs are ultimately the whole point of fiction. The change—the journey from one spiritual/emotional/intellectual place to another—is the story of humanity. As an author, your primary job is learning how those fundamental changes work in real life, and how you can then present them in your fiction with enough realism to connect with your readers.

WHY CHARACTER ARCS ARE NECESSARY TO TRANSFORM YOUR STORIES

Many writers struggle with the idea of "plot vs. character"—the idea that these two elements of a story supposedly stand in opposition to one another, or perhaps even cancel each other out. You may hear certain writers claiming their stories are either "plot-driven" or "character-driven"—as if a story can be only one or the other.

But as you're about to discover, this is an utterly false paradigm.

Character and plot are, in fact, two sides of the same coin. They cannot exist without each other. The external plot/conflict exists to provide a dramatic visual metaphor for the character's inner conflict. The story's inner and outer conflicts must mutually drive one another, pushing and pulling in the perfect symmetry of a piston pumping back and forth. The character creates the plot, and the plot forges the character.

Even better, if you look closely, what you find nestled at the heart of these two symbiotic halves of your story is *theme*. Theme arises directly from the character's arc, as proven within the exterior plot. What your character wants throughout your story and the ways in which he changes to either obtain it or grow past it is what will ultimately prove what your story is about. This is what proves your story's theme.

What this means is that the character's inner journey or arc can actually be structured in harmony with the plot itself. By breaking your story's three acts down into their nine most salient moments and turning points (Hook, Inciting Event, First Plot Point, First Pinch Point, Second Plot Point/Midpoint, Second Pinch Point, Third Plot Point, Climax, Resolution), you can then use these moments to not just guide your character's arc, but to ensure it aligns perfectly with the external plot.

In *Creating Character Arcs*, I used this basic approach to structure to identify and analyze five different types of arc. We find two positive arcs—the Positive Change Arc and Flat Arc. And we find three negative arcs—the Disillusionment Arc, Fall Arc, and Corruption Arc. Every single one of these arcs is based on the changes we all undergo or witness over and over again in real life. In learning to understand these universal psychological patterns, you can bring the resonance and power of realistic evolution to any type of story.

How to Use This Workbook

In this workbook, you will discover all of these principles, via step-by-step guides for crafting each important structural element and specific questions for narrowing your focus. If you're an outliner, you can use this workbook to help you plan powerful character arcs before you ever begin your first draft (the methods discussed here work hand in hand with those I teach in *Outlining Your Novel*, *Structuring Your Novel*, and their respective workbooks). You can also use the workbook to analyze an already completed manuscript, confirm its structural strengths, and identify its weaknesses.

Each chapter offers an introduction to the concepts discussed in the exercises, as well as examples from popular books and movies. I have also included a guide, at the end of each section's introduction, to help you locate the associated chapters in *Creating Character Arcs*. I recommend you start by reading that book—just as you would a textbook—before embarking on the workbook. You will understand the principles and their applicability better in context.

Each chapter of the workbook explores a different type of arc, from beginning to end. To determine which arc will be the best choice for your story, be sure to start with the section on the following page: "Choose Which Character Arc You Will Use."

Within each chapter, each section builds upon the next in a series of steps that will help you move from your character arc's big picture to the smaller details and back again. The more thorough you are in responding to each question and filling in each blank, the more prepared you will be to write or revise your novel. But don't hesitate to skip around. You may find you're unable to definitively answer some of the questions until you've first answered some of the later ones.

Your answers may require more space than what is provided here. Before you begin the exercises, grab a notebook so you can migrate your note-taking should you need more space.

An understanding of character arcs will allow you to harmonize character, plot, and theme to create stories that are cohesive and resonant wholes. Not only will you learn to skillfully entertain readers, you will be able to effortlessly open for them a window to the deeper world of humanity's primal struggles, downfalls, and victories.

CHOOSE WHICH CHARACTER ARC YOU WILL USE

I N THIS WORKBOOK, you will learn about the five major types of character arcs— Positive Change, Flat, and three variations of Negative Change (Disillusionment, Fall, and Corruption). Your first step is figuring out *which* of these arcs is right for your story.

Choosing your character's arc is every bit as important a decision as choosing the right plot. Get it wrong in the beginning, and, at best, you'll be facing massive rewrites. Some stories will pop into your brain with an obvious character arc already intact; other stories require a little more forethought.

Genre should always be a consideration, although it won't always be the deciding factor in the type of character arc you portray. Positive Change Arcs get happy endings, while Negative Change Arcs get sad endings. Broader "umbrella" genres such as fantasy, westerns, and historicals can tell just about any kind of story. But most romances, for example, are going to require a Positive Change or Flat Arc.

Remember, character arc is always *the final sum of your story's ending minus your story's beginning*. If you can figure out who your character is in either the beginning or ending of your story, you're already halfway to writing his arc.

(For more information on figuring out which arc is right for your character, see Chapter 21 in *Creating Character Arcs*.)

Fill out the following checklist to find the best options for your story:

HOW DOES YOUR STORY BEGIN?

☐ Your character begins your story in a comparatively good or happy place.

If so, he will be following one of these arcs:

- Flat Arc (in which he must leave that good place and fight for it when it is threatened)

- Disillusionment Arc (in which he must leave the happy place for a darker place)

- Corruption Arc (in which he must leave the good place for a dark place)

☐ Your character begins your story in a less-than-good place, in which he believes a Lie that is holding him back.

If so, he will be following one of these arcs:

- Positive Change Arc (in which he'll overcome the Lie and reach a positive Truth)

- Disillusionment Arc (in which he'll overcome the Lie and reach a negative Truth)

- Fall Arc (in which he'll never grow into the Truth, but instead embrace an even worse Lie)

☐ Your character begins your story in a comparatively less-than-good place, but already believes a Truth that has the potential to make him happy in spite of circumstances.

If so, he will be following one of these arcs:

- Flat Arc (in which he will use that Truth to transform the world around him)

- Corruption Arc (in which he will fall away from that Truth)

Write down the arc that best describes your intentions for your character: _____

_____.

How Does Your Story End?

Double-check your findings from the first round of questions against the following.

You chose...

☐ **Positive Change Arc:** Character ends in a better place, personally and physically, from where he started.

(If you checked this, skip to Chapter 1 after completing the rest of the exercises in this section.)

☐ **Flat Arc:** Character doesn't change personally, but the world and the supporting characters will change drastically from how they were in the beginning.

(If you checked this, skip to Chapter 2 after completing the rest of the exercises in this section.)

☐ **Disillusionment Arc:** Character ends in a place that's a darker reflection of his beginning.

(If you checked this, skip to Chapter 3 after completing the rest of the exercises in this section.)

☐ **Fall Arc**: Character ends in a place similar to the beginning, only worse.

(If you checked this, skip to Chapter 4 after completing the rest of the exercises in this section.)

☐ **Corruption Arc:** Character ends in a dark place that is the opposite of the good place in which he began.

(If you checked this, skip to Chapter 5 after completing the rest of the exercises in this section.)

Finesse your final choice of character arc by answering the following questions:

Is the arc you've identified your strongest possible option?

☐ Yes

☐ No

Why? _____

_____

_____

_____.

Do your story's beginning and ending contrast each other strongly enough?

☐ Yes

☐ No

Why? _____

_____

_____

_____.

If your protagonist had to face the events of the Climax in the beginning of the story, would he react to them in the same way he does at the end?

☐ Yes

☐ No

Why? _____

_____

_____

_____.

1

THE POSITIVE CHANGE ARC

CHARACTER BELIEVES LIE > OVERCOMES LIE >
NEW TRUTH IS LIBERATING

THE POSITIVE CHANGE Arc is arguably the most popular and resonant of all the three variations of character arc. This is also often called the heroic arc, in large part because it's basically the mythic evolution of personality popularly called the Hero's Journey. This type of arc results in an objectively happy ending, with the protagonist in a better place *personally* (in his interior life), regardless his exterior circumstances.

The Positive Change Arc, in its simplest manifestation, is all about the protagonist's changing priorities. The protagonist will start out with varying levels of personal unfulfillment and denial. Over the course of the story, he will be forced to challenge his beliefs about himself and the world, until finally he conquers his inner demons (and, as a result, probably his outer antagonists as well) and ends his arc having changed in a positive way.

He starts out believing a Lie that is holding him back from wholeness and empowerment, but thanks to the story journey he is about to enter, he will be forced into personal growth that will eventually allow him to reject the Lie and claim a healing (if sometimes still difficult) Truth.

The Positive Change Arc, as the most nuanced of the three arcs, provides the foundation for the Flat and Negative Arcs as well.

Positive Change Arc

CHARACTER BELIEVES LIE >
OVERCOMES LIE >
NEW TRUTH IS LIBERATING

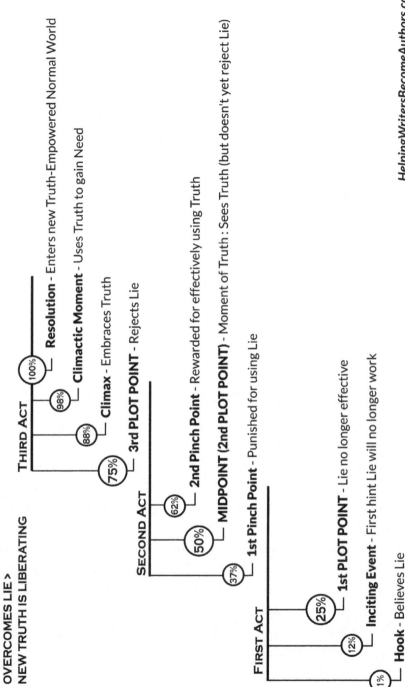

THIRD ACT

Resolution - Enters new Truth-Empowered Normal World

Climactic Moment - Uses Truth to gain Need

Climax - Embraces Truth

3rd PLOT POINT - Rejects Lie

2nd Pinch Point - Rewarded for effectively using Truth

MIDPOINT (2nd PLOT POINT) - Moment of Truth : Sees Truth (but doesn't yet reject Lie)

SECOND ACT

1st Pinch Point - Punished for using Lie

1st PLOT POINT - Lie no longer effective

Inciting Event - First hint Lie will no longer work

FIRST ACT

Hook - Believes Lie

100%
98%
88%
75%
62%
50%
37%
25%
12%
1%

HelpingWritersBecomeAuthors.com

THE LIE YOUR CHARACTER BELIEVES

IN ORDER FOR your character to evolve in a positive way, he must start out with something lacking in his life, some reason that makes change necessary. He is incomplete in some way, but not because he is lacking something external. Rather, your character is incomplete on the *inside*, thanks to the Lie He Believes.

He is harboring a deeply held misconception about himself, the world, or probably both. This misconception is going to prove a direct obstacle to his ability to fulfill his plot goal. In some instances, it may start out seeming to be a strength, but as the story progresses, it will become his Achilles heel.

Your character may not even realize he *has* a problem. In the First Act, his understanding of his deficiencies will be vague at best. He may not yet feel handicapped or even in denial about the Lie, until the Inciting Event (at the 12% mark) and/or the First Plot Point (at the 25% mark) rock his world and begin peeling away his defenses.

Your character's Lie may be further refined by adding qualifying elements— "provisos" the character has placed on the Lie. For instance, he may believe the Lie is true, but *only* under certain circumstances.

(For more information about the Lie Your Character Believes, see Chapter 1 in *Creating Character Arcs*.)

Write down four possible variations of the Lie Your Character Believes. Each one should be a specific belief, stated in one short sentence.

EXAMPLES:

- Might makes right.
  (*Thor*)

- The only way to earn love is through servitude.
  (*Jane Eyre*)

- Your only worth is in being the favorite.
  (*Toy Story*)

Lie #1: _____

_____

_____.

Lie #2: _____

_____

_____.

Lie #3: _____

_____

_____.

Lie #4: _____

_____

_____.

Are there any qualifying provisos to these Lies? (It's fine if there aren't.)

EXAMPLE:

- Jane Eyre's basic Lie is *she isn't worthy to be loved*, but it's qualified by her additional belief that *she can earn love if she is willing to enslave herself to others, physically and emotionally.*

Qualifier for Lie #1: _____

_____

_____.

Qualifier for Lie #2: _____

_____

_____.

Qualifier for Lie #3: _____

_____

_____.

Qualifier for Lie #4: _____

_____

_____.

How can each of these potential Lies be reflected in your character's exterior world and/or how can the exterior world be a metaphor for your character's inner struggle?

EXAMPLES:

- Thor's Lie of "right of kingship" is enforced in his glittering Normal World, as the son of the king.
- Jane Eyre's Lie of "love through servitude" is exemplified by her harsh upbringing under first her unloving aunt, then the harsh Lowood School for Girls.

Exterior World Reflection for Lie #1: _____

_____

_____

_____.

Exterior World Reflection for Lie #2: _____

_____

_____

_____.

Exterior World Reflection for Lie #3: _____

_____

_____

_____.

Exterior World Reflection for Lie #4: _____

_____

_____

_____.

Which of these four Lies will be the primary Lie for your character's arc? Which one best influences your plot and theme?

- ☐ Lie #1
- ☐ Lie #2
- ☐ Lie #3
- ☐ Lie #4

Final Choice of the Lie Your Character Believes: _____

_____

_____

_____.

SYMPTOMS OF THE LIE

HAVING TROUBLE FINDING the Lie? Look for the "symptoms" of the Lie in the character's life by considering his actions and especially his reactions. None of these symptoms *are* the Lie, but they're often products of the Lie.

Your protagonist may be aware of the symptoms of the Lie in his life, even if he isn't yet able to recognize the Lie itself. More than that, he may want nothing more than to shed the negative symptoms, but he *can't* because he can't get past his fundamental belief in the Lie.

EXAMPLES:

- Marcus Annan's Lie is *some sins are too great to be forgiven.* His symptoms are guilt, shame, secrets, and a destructive lifestyle.
  (*Behold the Dawn*)

- Ebenezer Scrooge's Lie is *a man's worth can only be measured by the amount of money he has earned.* His symptoms are greed, cruelty, selfishness, and an inability to forgive.
  (*A Christmas Carol*)

Answer the following questions to further hone the right Lie for your story.

Which of the following symptoms are present in your character's life?

☐ Fear
How is it manifesting? _____

_____

_____.

☐ Extreme hurt
How is it manifesting? _____

_____

_____.

☐ Inability to forgive

How is it manifesting? _____

_____

_____.

☐ Guilt

How is it manifesting? _____

_____

_____.

☐ Horrible secrets

How is it manifesting? _____

_____

_____.

☐ Shame over something the character did

How is it manifesting? _____

_____

_____.

☐ Shame over something done *to* the character

How is it manifesting? _____

_____

_____.

How is your character attempting to escape the pain caused by the symptoms of his Lie?

_____

_____

_____

_____.

How is your character's inability to face the Lie trapping her within the painful symptoms despite her efforts to escape them? _____

_____

_____

_____.

At the beginning of your story, what is your character lacking mentally, emotionally, or spiritually, as a result of the Lie? _____

_____

_____.

In your first chapter, how can you dramatize what he is lacking and/or suffering as a result of his Lie? _____

_____

_____.

If your character is *not* unhappy in the beginning of the story, how will the Inciting Event and/or the First Plot Point begin to make her uncomfortable as a result of her Lie? _____

_____

_____

_____.

THE THING YOUR CHARACTER NEEDS

T HE THING YOUR Character Needs is the *Truth*. This is her personalized antidote to the Lie. Even though she doesn't know it yet, this is the most important thing in her life. If she misses out on this Truth, she is never going to be able to grow in a positive way. She's either going to remain stuck in her current internal predicament forever, or she's going to digress into an even worse state (as happens in a Negative Change Arc).

Your character will spend most of the story pursuing an external plot goal related to the Thing She Wants (see page 33). But what the story is really about, on a deeper level, is her growth into a place where she, first subconsciously, then consciously, recognizes and pursues her internal goal—the Thing She Needs.

The Thing Your Character Needs usually won't be something physical—although it can (and usually should) take on a physical or visual manifestation by the end of the story. The Thing Your Character Needs is usually going to be nothing more than a realization. In some stories, this realization may change nothing about her external life, but it will always transform her perspective of herself and the world around her, giving her more capability to cope with her remaining external problems.

(For more information about the Thing Your Character Needs, see Chapter 2 in *Creating Character Arcs*.)

What Truth opposes the Lie Your Character Believes? _____

_____

_____.

EXAMPLES:

- Worthiness must be earned.
  (*Thor*)

- True love can be found only in freedom and wholeness of spirit.
  (*Jane Eyre*)

- Love only increases when it is shared.
  (*Toy Story*)

Write down four possible ways your story's Truth can manifest as a specific Thing Your Character Needs. This will be a specific action or belief on your character's part.

EXAMPLES:

- Learn humility and compassion.
  (*Thor*)

- Embrace spiritual freedom.
  (*Jane Eyre*)

- Willingly share Andy's love.
  (*Toy Story*)

Thing Your Character Needs #1: _____

_____

_____.

Thing Your Character Needs #2: _____

_____

_____.

Thing Your Character Needs #3: _____

_____

_____.

Thing Your Character Needs #4: _____

_____

_____.

How might your character *act* upon each of these four options at the end of the story, to demonstrate she has gained an understanding and acceptance of the Truth?

EXAMPLES:

- Sacrifices self to save others.
  (*Thor*)

- Refuses to enter an unequal marriage.
  (*Jane Eyre*)

- Rescues Buzz at risk of his own ability to return to Andy.
  (*Toy Story*)

Action based on Thing Your Character Needs #1: _____

_____

_____.

Action based on Thing Your Character Needs #2: _____

_____

_____.

Action based on Thing Your Character Needs #3: _____

_____

_____.

Action based on Thing Your Character Needs #4: _____

_____

_____.

Which of these four options will be the primary Thing Your Character Needs in this story? Which one best reflects your story's Truth?

☐ Thing Your Character Needs #1
☐ Thing Your Character Needs #2
☐ Thing Your Character Needs #3
☐ Thing Your Character Needs #4

Final Choice of the Thing Your Character Needs: _____

_____

_____

_____.

At the end of the story, will the Thing Your Character Needs:

☐ change your character's external circumstances for the better?

☐ change your character's ability to appreciate or cope with existing external circumstances?

How do you see the Truth manifesting externally/visually at the end of your story?

_____

_____

_____.

EXAMPLES:

- Thor is at peace with his father.
  (*Thor*)

- Jane enters, as a spiritually empowered person, into a marriage with Rochester.
  (*Jane Eyre*)

- Woody is friends with Buzz and no longer nervous about the arrival of new toys.
  (*Toy Story*)

THE THING YOUR CHARACTER WANTS

THE THING YOUR Character Wants will almost always be something external, something physical. The character is trying to salve his inner emptiness with exterior solutions. His problem is depression, but instead of seeking the Truth and the Thing He Needs as the true cure, he's busily putting a cast on his arm. He thinks if he can just have that new job, that new trophy wife, that new set of golf clubs, everything will be perfect. He'll be rich, powerful, loved, respected, and fulfilled.

(For more information about the Thing Your Character Wants, see Chapter 2 in *Creating Character Arcs*.)

Write down four possible Things Your Character Wants. These are deep primal desires. They are *not* necessarily your character's story goal, but will influence the specific goal.

EXAMPLES:

- Be king.
  (*Thor*)

- Be loved.
  (*Jane Eyre*)

- Be Andy's favorite toy.
  (*Toy Story*)

Desire #1: _____

_____

_____.

Desire #2: _____

_____

_____.

Desire #3: _____

_____

_____.

Desire #4: _____

_____

_____.

How are each of these desires influenced by a symptom of the Lie?

Desire #1: _____

_____

_____.

Desire #2: _____

_____

_____.

Desire #3: _____

_____

_____.

Desire #4: _____

_____

_____.

What specific story goal arises from each of these desires? This will be the plot goal your character will be working toward over the course of your entire story.

EXAMPLES:

- Return to Asgard so he can be king.
  (*Thor*)

- Be with Rochester.
  (*Jane Eyre*)

- Get rid of Buzz.
  (*Toy Story*)

Goal Arising From Desire #1: _____

_____

_____.

Goal Arising From Desire #2: _____

_____

_____.

Goal Arising From Desire #3: _____

_____

_____.

Goal Arising From Desire #4: _____

_____

_____.

Which of these four desires will be the primary Thing Your Character Wants in this story? Which one best guides your plot and theme?

☐ Desire #1
☐ Desire #2
☐ Desire #3
☐ Desire #4

Final Choice of the Thing Your Character Wants: _____

_____

_____.

Which of the four goals will be your character's primary plot goal in this story? Which one best represents the Thing He Wants and drives your plot?

☐ Goal #1
☐ Goal #2
☐ Goal #3
☐ Goal #4

Final Choice of Character's Plot Goal: _____

_____

_____.

Will your character have to:

☐ sacrifice the Thing He Wants in order to gain the Thing He Needs?

☐ gain the Thing He Wants only after first embracing the Thing He Needs?

How? _____

_____

_____

_____.

YOUR CHARACTER'S GHOST

YOUR CHARACTER'S "GHOST" is something in his past that haunts him. You may also see it sometimes referred to as the "wound." This Ghost is the *reason* the character believes in the Lie. Often, the wound will be something shocking and traumatic, but it can also be something small and ordinary, such as a stressful parental relationship or a physical inferiority. The bigger and more destructive the Lie, the more shocking and impactful the Ghost should be. Or to flip that on its head: the bigger the Ghost, the bigger the Lie, the bigger the arc.

(For more information about the Ghost, see Chapter 3 in *Creating Character Arcs*.)

Write down four possible events that might have happened in your character's past to traumatize him and/or give him a twisted view of the world or himself.

EXAMPLES:

- The promise that Thor would grow up to be king, regardless his personal merits.
  (*Thor*)

- Jane's aunt's refusal to love her.
  (*Jane Eyre*)

- Knowledge of what happens to unloved toys.
  (*Toy Story*)

Ghost #1: _____

_____

_____.

Ghost #2: _____

_____

_____.

Ghost #3: _____

_____.

Ghost #4: _____

_____.

Which of these four Ghosts will be the primary motivating wound in your character's backstory?

 ☐ Ghost #1
 ☐ Ghost #2
 ☐ Ghost #3
 ☐ Ghost #4

Which of the following best describes your chosen Ghost?

 ☐ An ingrained belief.

EXAMPLE:

- During Jane's childhood, her aunt tells her over and over again she is wicked and worthless.
  (*Jane Eyre*)

 ☐ Something the character did.

EXAMPLE:

- During the French and Indian War, Benjamin Martin massacred and dismembered the enemy.
  (*The Patriot*)

 ☐ Something done *to* the character.

EXAMPLE:

- Peter Parker witnessed his uncle's murder.
  (*Spider-Man*)

 ☐ An ignorant or apathetic belief or position harmful to others.

EXAMPLE:

- A king's power must be enforced by right of war.
  (*Thor*)

How does your chosen Ghost directly create or enable the Lie Your Character Believes? _____

_____

_____.

How is the character using the Lie to try to compensate for, cover up, or simply survive the consequences of the Ghost? _____

_____

_____.

How does the Ghost tie in thematically with the Lie Your Character Believes? __

_____

_____.

On a scale of 1 to 10, how "big" is the Ghost?
    1. ☐ (e.g., Stressful Parental Relationship)
    2. ☐
    3. ☐
    4. ☐
    5. ☐
    6. ☐
    7. ☐
    8. ☐
    9. ☐
    10. ☐ (e.g., Murder of a Loved One)

How is your Lie (and thus the degree of change your character must undergo) commensurate to the "size" of the Ghost (e.g., a big Ghost gets a big Lie)? _____

_____

_____.

How will your story's Truth be able to "heal" the character of the Ghost's effects? __

_____

_____.

Must readers explicitly understand the Ghost in order for the rest of the story to make sense?

    ☐ Yes

    ☐ No

This Ghost will best be shared with readers how?

    ☐ As a mystery (teased in the beginning and revealed later at an important turning point in the plot)

    ☐ Dramatized at the beginning of the First Act

    ☐ Not shared at all

THE CHARACTERISTIC MOMENT

THE ACTUAL STRUCTURE of the character arc begins with the Characteristic Moment. The Characteristic Moment aligns with the structural Hook, which shows up the moment your protagonist does—presumably in the first chapter.

The Characteristic Moment is your protagonist's big debut. He steps onto the stage, the spotlight hits him—and he shines. In this one moment, he shows readers what he's all about: the good, the bad, and the potential for greatness to come. The Characteristic Moment shows readers exactly why this protagonist is going to be worth reading about.

(For more information about the Characteristic Moment, see Chapter 4 in *Creating Character Arcs*.)

EXAMPLES:

- A vow, as a child, to be like his father and grow up to "fight them all," and then, as an adult, a cocky display on his way to being announced heir to the throne—which illustrates key personality traits, the effects of the Lie, and the Thing He Wants Most.
  (*Thor*)

- A lonely moment, banned from the family circle, spent reading, and then a refusal to submit to her cousin's unjust cruelty—which illustrates both the Ghost and key personality traits.
  (*Jane Eyre*)

- A montage showing Woody being lovingly played with by Andy, and then, once he's "awake," a calm and organized leadership of the other toys—which illustrates the Thing He Wants Most and key personality traits.
  (*Toy Story*)

Before you can craft the perfect Characteristic Moment, you must first know something about your character. Answer the following questions for starters (and for a full character interview, see my books *Outlining Your Novel* and the *Outlining Your Novel Workbook*).

What is this character's role in the story?

☐ Protagonist   ☐ Sidekick

☐ Antagonist   ☐ Love Interest

☐ Mentor   ☐ Other: _____

What is your character's name? _____.

How old is your character? _____.

Of what nationality is your character? _____.

What is your character's occupation or primary identity (e.g., mom, rebel soldier)? __

_____.

Does the character have any important physical characteristics (e.g., a limp)? _____

_____

_____.

Name three prevailing aspects of the character's personality (e.g., kindness, quick temper):

1. _____.

2. _____.

3. _____.

What *one* important personality trait, virtue, or skill best sums up your character? ___

_____

_____

_____.

How can you dramatize this aspect of your character to its fullest extent? _____

_____

_____.

How can you dramatize this aspect in a way that also introduces the plot? _____

_____

_____.

What do you want readers to find most sympathetic and/or interesting about this character?

_____

_____.

How can you dramatize this aspect of your character in an opening scene? ____

_____

_____.

What is your character's overall story goal (the Thing He Wants Most)?_____

_____

_____.

How can you set up this goal or show the coming need for it in an opening scene?

_____

_____

_____.

What is your character's scene goal in the opening chapter? _____

_____

_____.

How will you dramatize this scene goal right from the start of your opening

scene? _____

_____.

How will the character's pursuit of this goal meet with an obvious obstacle (i.e.,

conflict)? _____

_____

_____.

How will this goal move the plot, either by immediately causing consequences or

setting them up for later? _____

_____

_____.

How can any of the above help you demonstrate, or at least hint at, your character's

Lie? _____

_____.

How can you reveal or at least hint at your character's Ghost? _____

_____

_____

_____.

How can you craft the above elements to make your protagonist immediately appealing to readers (e.g., what's keeping them from looking away?)?_____

_____

_____

_____.

Which of your character's strengths can you show readers right away? _____

_____

_____.

Which of your character's pertinent weaknesses (especially Lie-driven weaknesses) can you show readers right away? _____

_____

_____.

List events or activities you can use in your opening chapter to dramatize all the of above. Try to think of "big" moments that are unique, visually engaging, and keep the characters in motion.

1. _____.

2. _____.

3. _____.

4. _____.

5. _____.

Write a summary of your opening chapter and how you will introduce your character in

a memorable and engaging Characteristic Moment: _____

_____

_____

_____

_____

_____

_____

_____

_____

_____

_____

_____

_____

_____

_____

_____

_____

_____

_____.

Which of the following does your proposed Characteristic Moment accomplish?

☐ Introduce character.

☐ Reveal character's name.

☐ Indicate character's gender.

☐ Indicate character's age group.

☐ Indicate character's nationality.

☐ Indicate character's occupation/main identity.

☐ Indicate any important physical characteristics.

☐ Indicate role in the story (i.e., protagonist).

☐ Demonstrate prevailing aspect of personality.

☐ Hook readers' sympathy and/or interest.

☐ Demonstrate scene goal.

☐ Indicate story goal.

☐ Demonstrate (or at least hint at) Lie.

☐ Move plot directly or through foreshadowing.

If you're unable to combine the majority of the above elements into one scene, answer whether it would work better to divide the necessary characteristic elements into two or more scenes, _____

_____

_____

_____

_____.

THE NORMAL WORLD

THE CHARACTERIST MOMENT is only half of a good character arc's opening. It gives readers a character, but the character still needs context. The Normal World provides that context. At its most basic level, the Normal World is—as its name suggests—a setting. This is the place in which your story opens. It is a place in which your character has found contentment—or at least complacency.

The Normal World plays a vital role in grounding the First Act of your story in a concrete setting. Even more important, the Normal World creates the standard against which all the personal and plot changes to come will be measured. Without this vivid opening example of what will change in your character's life, the rest of the arc will lack definition and potency.

(For more information about the Normal World, see Chapter 5 in *Creating Character Arcs*.)

EXAMPLES:

- A peaceful and prosperous planet—which enables the protagonist's prideful misconceptions.
  (*Thor*)

- A stark and loveless childhood, first at Jane's aunt's, then at a boarding school for girls—which reinforces her belief in her unloveableness.
  (*Jane Eyre*)

- Andy's room, where Woody is the boss—which reinforces his belief in the Lie.
  (*Toy Story*)

Start by determining what type of Normal World will best set up your character's arc. Which of the following do you think will work best?

☐ Normal World seems wonderful on the surface in the First Act, but as the story progresses, its perfect façade will crack open right alongside the protagonist's misconceptions about the world and herself.

EXAMPLE:

- A seemingly perfect neighborhood of conformity is revealed for its close-mindedness and bigotry.
  (*Edward Scissorshands*)

How might you create this type of Normal World for your story? _____

_____

_____

_____.

☐ Normal World is safe but boring, with the protagonist chafing ineffectually against it, making no real effort to move on.

EXAMPLE:

- Luke Skywalker insists he wants to escape his home on a backwater moisture farm, even though he has never made any real concerted effort to do so.
  (*Star Wars: A New Hope*)

How might you create this type of Normal World for your story?_____

_____

_____

_____.

☐ Normal World is an unhappy place, but the protagonist is at least temporarily stuck there against her will.

EXAMPLE:

- The Allied protagonists are confined against their will in a Germansu-per-prison during World War II.
  (*The Great Escape*)

How might you create this type of Normal World for your story?_____

_____

_____.

☐ Normal World is a legitimately good place, but the protagonist isn't yet ready to appreciate it or is being temporarily held back by the advantages he is receiving there.

- George Bailey lives in a lovely small town full of kind and caring people, but he continues to view it only as a prison holding him back from bigger dreams and adventures.
(*It's a Wonderful Life*)

How might you create this type of Normal World for your story? _____

_____

_____

_____.

☐ Normal World presents a set of challenges the protagonist finds himself unequipped to deal with until *after* he's experienced life beyond the Normal World (the character will always return to the Normal World at the end in this type of story).

- The elderly protagonist refuses to leave his lifetime home, eventhough he is no longer happy there without his beloved late wife, and even though his increasing age makes living alone difficult.
(*Up*)

How might you create this type of Normal World for your story? _____

_____

_____

_____.

Briefly describe the physical setting of the Normal World (e.g., Chicago or Mars): ___

_____.

How does your chosen Normal World symbolically represent the Lie Your Character

Believes? _____

_____.

Example:

- A neurotic and dangerous city—NYC—represents and reinforces general neuroticism about everything and will contrast neatly against the later motif of "taking a vacation from your problems."
  (*What About Bob?*)

How will the Normal World visibly prove to readers (*show* them) your protagonist's "be-

fore" state at the beginning of the story? _____

_____

_____.

What setting for the Normal World provides the most logical backstory for *why* your

character believes the Lie? _____

_____.

What is holding your protagonist in the Normal World that has kept him from leav-

ing it before now? _____

_____

_____.

How is your chosen Normal World empowering your character to continue believing his Lie by giving him no reason to look beyond it? _____

_____

_____

_____

_____.

How will the Normal World contrast with the Adventure World that will follow in the next two acts? _____

_____

_____

_____.

Which of the following will best describe the Adventure World of your story's main conflict?

☐ A dramatically new and different setting.

EXAMPLE:

- Jane leaves Lowood School to be a governess at Thornfield Hall. (*Jane Eyre*)

☐ The same physical setting as the Normal World, with only facets of the world changing.

EXAMPLE:

- The arrival of the little girl Boo throws the existing Normal World of Monstropolis into chaos. (*Monsters, Inc.*)

When your protagonist is later forced out of the Normal World into the Second Act,

how will this begin to shake his belief in the Lie? _____

_____

_____

_____.

Will the character return to the Normal World at the end of the story?

☐ Yes

☐ No

If the Normal World remains a legitimately good place, how will the protagonist

need to change in order to appreciate it? _____

_____

_____

_____.

If the Normal World remains an unchanged destructive place, how will the pro-

tagonist have moved past its control over him? _____

_____

_____

_____.

If the protagonist impacted the Normal World over the course of the story, how

will it have changed in the end? _____

_____

_____

_____

_____

_____.

THE FIRST ACT

WHERE DOES IT BELONG?

From the 1% mark to the 25% mark in your story.

T HE MOST IMPORTANT thing to understand about the First Act is that it is setup. Once you've hooked your readers' interest in the first chapter, the main responsibility of the First Act is to lay the groundwork for everything that follows. Without that, the rest of the story will (at best) lack context and resonance.

Within the First Act, your primary job is to introduce all characters who will be important catalysts within the conflict, as many prominent settings as possible, the protagonist's personal dilemma and goal, the main conflict and the antagonistic force driving it, and the stakes if the protagonist fails within the conflict.

The introduction of these things early on is important because it prevents the random or coincidental appearance of people, items, places, and events in the Second and Third Acts. It also creates context for the readers' questions about the conflict, which will prevent unnecessary confusion. Finally, it plants foreshadowing for important revelations later on.

(For more information about the First Act in a Positive Change Arc, see Chapter 6 in *Creating Character Arcs*.)

How will you reinforce/dramatize the character's Lie in the first chapter? _____

_____

_____

_____.

EXAMPLE:

- Thor's Lie is practically handed to him by his father who tells him straight out he was born to be king.
  (*Thor*)

How will you show how the character's internal problems are, in turn, causing external problems? _____

_____.

How will you demonstrate the Thing Your Character Wants and the Thing She Needs? _____

_____

_____.

How will her Characteristic Moment illustrate or hint at the Lie? _____

_____

_____

_____.

How will her Normal World immediately illustrate or hint at the Lie? _____

_____

_____

_____.

Name three ways you will continue to reinforce the Lie or introduce more of its facets throughout the First Act:

    1. _____.

    2. _____.

    3. _____.

How can you hint at your character's latent capability for positive change? _____

_____

_____

_____.

Example:

- Woody's ability to be a good friend is on display right from the start in his caring attitude toward the other toys in Andy's room—even if he's not yet ready to be a good friend to Buzz.
  (*Toy Story*)

What specific quality will be intrinsic to your character's ability to fight his way out

of the Lie? _____.

Even if this trait isn't yet fully developed, how can you hint right from the beginn-

ing that the seed is there? _____

_____

_____.

How can you begin giving the character small hints about the destructive nature of

the Lie and the positive nature of the Truth? _____

_____

_____

_____.

- The cure (love and family) for Bob Wiley's Lie (people will only pay attention to you if they think you're crazy) is strongly foreshadowed through his immediate connection with Leo's family photographs. (*What About Bob?*)

What Inciting Event will be the Call to Adventure that first brushes your character

against the main conflict halfway through the First Act (at the 12% mark)? _____

_____

_____.

EXAMPLE:

- Theme-park owner John Hammond suggests protagonist Dr. Grant postpone his paleontology dig in order to come and "pen a wee testimonial" for his new theme park. (*Jurassic Park*)

How will this Inciting Event set up the character's entry into the Adventure World

of the main conflict in the Second Act? _____

_____

_____.

Does the Inciting Event initially seem:

☐ a good thing.

☐ a bad thing.

How will the Call to Adventure initially be met with resistance or refusal? _____

_____

_____.

- Dr. Grant's first response to Hammond's preposterous offer is to turn him down flat. Although he gets over it quickly enough when Hammond raises the stakes, his initial reluctance is important to the story's emotional pacing.

Will the protagonist be the one to initially reject the Call to Adventure, or will some

one else try to reject it for him? _____.

How long will it take the protagonist to stop resisting?

    ☐ Entire rest of the First Act up to the First Plot Point.

    ☐ Shorter period ending with what event? _____.

How does the Inciting Event change the protagonist's awareness of and comfort in

the Normal World in however small or subconscious a way? _____

_____

_____.

Toward the end of the First Act, how will your protagonist still be entrenched in the

Lie? _____

_____.

How will his subconscious attitude toward the positivity of the Truth take its first step

forward? _____

_____

_____.

EXAMPLE:

- At the end of her First Act, Jane still believes she must serve to be worthy of love. But now she decides she'd rather strike out on her own and take service as a governess, instead of continuing to drudge as a teacher at Lowood School.
  (*Jane Eyre*)

What will the protagonist decide to *do* about the Call to Adventure at the Inciting

Event? _____

_____

_____

_____

_____.

EXAMPLE:

- At the end of the First Act, Walter decides to give up on running away and instead returns to live with his uncles. This isn't a passive decision; it's an active choice, which now makes him a willing resident on the farm for the first time in the story.
  (*Secondhand Lions*)

THE FIRST PLOT POINT

WHERE DOES IT BELONG?

25% of the way into your story.

IF THE FIRST Act is setup, then the First Plot Point is the point of no return. This is where the setup ends and the conflict begins "for real." At this point, the character commits—usually because she has no choice—to a decision that will propel her out of the comfortable stagnation of the Normal World and the Lie She Believes. Visualize a locked door separating the First Act from the Second Act. The First Plot Point is where the protagonist sticks her key in that door and unlocks it.

The First Plot Point belongs around the 20-25% mark, where your character leaves her Normal World, ending the setup of your First Act. The First Plot Point either incorporates or is directly followed by the character's decision to react in a strong and irrevocable way. Usually, it will be a major scene.

(For more information about the First Plot Point in a Positive Change Arc, see Chapter 7 in *Creating Character Arcs*.)

What event occurs at the end of the First Act that causes your character to leave the

Normal World and irreversibly engage with the main conflict? _____

_____

_____.

EXAMPLES:

- After Thor nearly incites a war, his father banishes him from his majestic Normal World and sends him to live on Earth as a mortal. (*Thor*)

- Jane is given a position as governess at the stately but mysterious Thornfield Hall, where she first encounters her brusque but fair employer, Mr. Rochester. (*Jane Eyre*)

- After Andy's birthday party, Woody is knocked from his place of honor on the bed by cool new toy Buzz. (*Toy Story*)

In what way might this event be surprising even after the Inciting Event? _____

_____

_____

_____.

Which of the following best describes your First Plot Point?

☐   A seemingly positive opportunity.

EXAMPLE:

- Ender graduates to the next level in Battle School.
  (*Ender's Game*)

☐   Something disastrous.

EXAMPLE:

- Benjamin's son is murdered by British soldiers and his plantation burned and looted.
  (*The Patriot*)

What decision on your character's part led him right up to the First Plot Point,

making him at least partially responsible for what happens? (See also the final

question in the last section.) _____

_____

_____.

EXAMPLE:

- Thor decides to attack the neighboring planet Jodenheim in what is construed as an act of war (leading to his banishment).

- Jane decides to apply for a position outside of her current employment as a teacher at Lowood school (leading to her new life at Thornfield Hall).

- Benjamin chooses to care for the wounded and dying Continental soldiers, after a battle was fought outside his property (leading to the British burning his plantation, capturing one son, and murdering another).

Which of the following best describes your First Plot Point?

☐ It destroys the Normal World, leaving the protagonist no choice but to move on.

EXAMPLE:

- The protagonist's plantation home is ransacked and burned by British soldiers.

☐ It physically removes the protagonist from the Normal World.

EXAMPLE:

- Jane voluntarily leaves her Normal World at Lowood School to enter the Adventure World of her employment with Mr. Rochester.

☐ It warps the Normal World, forcing the protagonist to adapt to new ways of surviving within it.

EXAMPLE:

- Peter Parker's physical setting of New York City does not change, but after his uncle is murdered, his life within that setting is entirely different.
  (*Spider-Man*)

Which best describes your protagonist's reaction to the First Plot Point?

☐ Enthusiasm—she wants to enter the conflict of the Second Act.

☐ Resistance—she has to be forced to enter the conflict of the Second Act.

After the First Plot Point, how will your protagonist react? _____

_____

_____

_____.

What definitive action will he take to move forward into the Adventure World of

the main conflict? _____

_____.

Which will the character be trying to do?

☐ Restore the old normal.

How: _____.

☐ Find a new normal.

How: _____.

Name three new physical needs that must be met in the aftermath of the First Plot Point:

1. _____.

2. _____.

3. _____.

What definitive new plot goal will the character now adopt (something quantifiable,

based on the Thing He Wants)? _____

_____

_____.

Do you want the character to ultimately achieve this goal?

☐ Yes.
   Why? _____.

☐ No.
   Why? _____.

How will the character's decisions and actions in the aftermath of the First Plot Point drag her out of complacency and force her onto a path toward eventually destroying her Lie? _____

_____

_____

_____.

What about the Adventure World of the Second Act makes the character's Lie less comfortable than it was in the Normal World? _____

_____

_____

_____

_____.

THE FIRST HALF OF THE SECOND ACT

WHERE DOES IT BELONG?

From the 25% mark to the 50% mark in your story.

I N THE STRUCTURE of character arcs, the First Half of the Second Act is where your character ventures (or is thrust) into uncharted territory—and gets lost. He may not quite see it that way himself, but this is where he begins to discover that the old rules (the Lie He Believes) no longer apply.

This puts him in a bit of a tailspin. He scrambles to react to the events of the First Plot Point, while chasing as hard as ever after the Thing He Wants. He's reactive in the sense that he's at the mercy of the antagonistic force; he is not in control of the conflict. But don't confuse reactivity with passivity. Your character will be *very* active in his pursuit of his goals during this time, and he'll be learning which methods of achieving that goal are ineffective. This new knowledge will, in turn, lay the groundwork for helping him begin to realize how his belief in the Lie is holding him back.

(For more information about the First Half of the Second Act in a Positive Change Arc, see Chapter 8 in *Creating Character Arcs*.)

What "tools" (in the form of information from another character) will your character begin to receive that offer hints for how to start fighting his Lie? _____

_____

_____

_____.

EXAMPLE:

- Bo Peep encourages a marginalized (and slightly hysterical) Woody by telling him, "I know Andy's excited about Buzz, but you know he'll always have a special place for you."
  (*Toy Story*)

How can other characters *show* your protagonist the Truth, rather than just *telling* her about it?_____

_____

_____

_____

_____.

How is your protagonist feeling slightly out of place within the new Adventure World of the Second Act? _____

_____

_____.

What old Lie-based actions is the protagonist still trying to use to reach his goals? ___

_____

_____

_____.

How are these old Lie-based actions proving less effective in the Second Act than they did in the First? _____

_____

_____

_____.

- After Thor finds himself banished to Earth, his old attitude as an arrogant immortal has him attempting to muscle his way to authority—and failing in a variety of humiliating ways (getting tasered, sedated, and run over).
  (*Thor*)

How is the protagonist demonstrating confusion or frustration about why his

old methods are no longer working for him? _____

_____

_____.

What first move will he make to slowly begin evolving his tactics to avoid these Lie-

based failures? _____

_____

_____.

How is the character pursuing the Thing She Wants in the Second Act? _____

_____

_____.

How is she getting closer to achieving her plot goal? _____

_____

_____

_____.

How is her pursuit of the Thing She Wants pushing her away from the Thing She Needs?_____

_____

_____.

If the character continues down this path unchecked, what personal, spiritual, and perhaps even physical destruction would she end up running into? _____

_____

_____

_____.

EXAMPLE:

- The three Gulf-War soldiers find the Iraqi gold bullion they've been searching for, steal it, and head out of town. They've got what they want, but they're leaving an entire Shiite village at the mercy of enemy soldiers, making them no better than the men they've risked their lives fighting.
(*Three Kings*)

How can you give your character a tiny glimpse of what life would be like without his Lie? _____

_____

_____.

EXAMPLE:

- Matt fights alongside his brother-in-law's football firm and learns, for the first time, how good it feels to fight back when someone pushes you around.
(*Green Street Hooligans*)

THE MIDPOINT

WHERE DOES IT BELONG?

50% of the way into your story.

YOUR PROTAGONIST WILL have spent the First Half of the Second Act blundering around in foreign territory, making mistakes based on false assumptions, and getting his hand slapped for his every wrong move. But he's also going to have been slowly—maybe even subconsciously—learning his lesson and figuring things out. These personal revelations are going to lead him up to a very special turning point at the story's Midpoint, 50% of the way into the story.

In discussions of plot structure, the Midpoint's emphasis is always placed on the protagonist's shift from a reactive role (not in control of the conflict) to an active role (taking control of the conflict). This is the fundamental turning point in your book. Without this shift, you have no evolution, no variety, and no story. But taken at face value, this explanation of the Midpoint is incomplete. Where, after all, does this shift come from? It comes from deep inside the character. It comes from the heart of his character arc: the Moment of Truth.

(For more information about the Midpoint in a Positive Change Arc, see Chapter 9 in *Creating Character Arcs*.)

What is your story's Midpoint event? _____

_____

_____.

EXAMPLES:

- A battle in the government's SHIELD complex to reclaim his hammer Mjolnir.
  (*Thor*)

- A bizarre nighttime attack upon an uninvited guest in Rochester's house.
  (*Jane Eyre*)

- A brawl that leaves both toys stranded at a gas station.
  (*Toy Story*)

What can you do to make this centerpiece scene as "big" as possible? _____

_____

_____

_____.

How have the events of the First Half of the Second Act led up to the Midpoint by slowly helping your protagonist see the benefit of no longer using as many Lie-based tactics to reach his goal? _____

_____

_____.

How will the external events of the Midpoint prompt a "Moment of Truth," in which the character sees the benefits of the Truth and embraces them? _____

_____

_____

_____.

EXAMPLES:

- When Thor discovers he is physically unable to lift his hammer, he realizes strength and right of birth alone do not make him worthy to wield it.

- When Jane realizes Rochester's growing dependence upon her after he trusts her with their wounded guest, she realizes she cannot continue to work for him if he is to marry someone else.

- When Woody's jealousy-fueled assault on Buzz leaves them stranded, he realizes he cannot return to his owner Andy if he isn't willing to save Buzz too.

How will the Moment of Truth prompt the character to turn away from the *effects* of

the Lie in her life? _____

_____

_____.

How will the character still remain unwilling to completely reject the Lie it-

self? _____

_____

_____.

EXAMPLE:

- After the Midpoint, in which he (somewhat accidentally) helps his psychiatrist's son learn to dive, Bob grows in confidence. But even as his symptoms decrease, he still takes for granted the Lie that he is actually crazy.

During the rest of the Second Act, how will you demonstrate your character's

deepening inner conflict—caught between Lie and Truth? _____

_____

_____.

What is the character still failing to understand about the total nature of the

Truth that will prevent him from being able to fully implement it? _____

_____

_____.

How will this realization help the character better understand the true nature of the conflict (and thus be better equipped to conquer it)? _____

_____

_____

_____.

How will the events of the Midpoint act as a swivel between the two halves of your story—shifting your character out of uninformed reaction and into educated action?

_____

_____

_____.

How will the character's continuing inner conflict and incomplete understanding of the Truth prevent him from achieving total victory while still in the Second Act?

_____

_____

_____

_____.

THE SECOND HALF OF THE SECOND ACT

WHERE DOES IT BELONG?

From the 50% mark to the 75% mark in your story.

THE SECOND HALF of the Second Act is where your character shifts out of the reactive phase (in which the conflict is being controlled by the antagonist) and moves into the active phase (in which he starts taking control of the conflict for himself).

When he learned the Truth at the Midpoint, it allowed him to start implementing the correct actions to get the desired results in his quest for the plot goal. Thanks to that major personal revelation at the Midpoint, he now *gets it*. He charges ahead, thinking he now sees clearly. But the key thing to remember about this section of the story is that your character is still half-blinded by the Lie. He's charging into the conflict, believing he now has 20/20 vision, when really he only has one eye open.

(For more information about the Second Half of the Second Act in a Positive Change Arc, see Chapter 10 in *Creating Character Arcs*.)

How is the character acting on the Truth she discovered at the Midpoint? _____

_____

_____.

What new "tools" did the Moment of Truth provide your character that are allowing

him to make better progress toward the Thing He Wants? _____

_____

_____

_____.

What obstacles will the antagonistic force still be putting in his way? _____

_____

_____

_____.

EXAMPLE:

- Being accepted by Leo's family has empowered Bob, and he starts to come alive in the Second Half of the Second Act, as he charismatically salvages Leo's disastrous Good Morning America interview, then charms the staff at the psychiatric hospital after Leo tries to involuntarily commit him.
  (*What About Bob?*)

How is the Lie still present in the character's life, if only on a subconscious level? ___

_____

_____.

How is the character suffering cognitive dissonance as the result of clinging to

two incompatible beliefs? _____

_____

_____.

How is his refusal to completely face the Lie holding him back from fully com

mitting to the Truth? _____

_____

_____.

What mistakes is the protagonist making within the conflict as a result of the

Lie's continuing presence and his resultant inner conflict? _____

_____

_____.

EXAMPLE:

- Woody has committed to the Truth that he must rescue Buzz if he's to return to Andy. But the Lie that fuels his jealousy and hatred of Buzz is still alive and well. He's not helping Buzz because he wants to; he's helping him because he has to. He drags Buzz along without ever stopping to consider him as an equal or to wonder what's up with his sudden change in personality after Buzz sees the toy commercial on TV. Woody's Lie continues to get in his way, even as the Truth enables him to make decided progress.

How is the character being drawn more and more to the Thing He Needs? _____

_____

_____.

In what way might he start acting more selflessly? _____

_____

_____

_____.

In moving *toward* the Thing He Needs, how might he be moving *away* from the

Thing He Wants? _____

_____.

- The three Gulf-War soldiers still want the Iraqi gold bullion. They're just as determined as ever to smuggle every last brick back to the States. But their actions now have an entirely different focus: they're committed to helping the Shiite villagers get across the border to safety before they go back for their gold.
(*Three Kings*)

Write down four scenes from the first half of the story in which your character demonstrated Lie-driven motives. Then brainstorm four scenes you can include in the second half that will contrast the earlier scenes by showing how your character's new understanding of the Truth has already started to change her.

"Before" Scenes   **"After" Scenes**

1. _____   1. _____

2. _____   2. _____

3. _____   3. _____

4. _____   4. _____

EXAMPLE:

- **Before:** Thor wantonly and carelessly plunges his friends into battle against the Frost Giants and nearly gets them killed.

- **After:** When his friends later risk a journey to Earth to rescue him, he expresses his gratefulness to see them again but tells them they should not have endangered themselves for him. He proves how his "always attack" mindset in the first half has evolved when he admits the comparative weakness of his mortal body and chooses to help evacuate the townspeople rather than join the fight with his friends.
(*Thor*)

At the end of the Second Act, how will the Thing the Character Wants place itself within the character's grasp, offering a seeming victory? _____

_____.

EXAMPLE:

- Jane Eyre seems to get exactly what she wants when she agrees to marry Rochester. She's found someone she loves who adores her back. She never expected to be loved, and yet, out of the clear blue sky, all her wildest dreams are about to come true. (*Jane Eyre*)

Why will it be necessary for the character to subject himself to the Lie once again in

order to claim the Thing He Wants? _____

_____

_____

_____.

How will the character have to sacrifice the Thing He Needs in order to gain

the Thing He Wants at this point? _____

_____

_____

_____.

How can you dramatize the character's inner conflict in this section? _____

_____

_____

_____

_____.

How will the character be able to convince himself, at least temporarily, that

the Thing He Wants is *not* an obstacle to the Thing He Needs? _____

_____

_____

_____.

EXAMPLE:

- Jane agrees to marry Rochester, but deep inside, she's not at peace. She senses, almost right away, that in marrying Rochester she is once again sacrificing her independence of spirit and enslaving herself. She wants to be with him so much she throws the Truth right back out the window and clings to the Lie that emotional and physical servitude must be the price for love.

Before the Second Act ends, how can you blatantly demonstrate the crux of your

character's arc? _____

_____

_____

_____.

EXAMPLE:

- Walter's uncle shares a small part of the speech he likes to give young men, and it just so happens that the part he shares applies directly to Walter's fear of putting his faith in the people he loves: "Sometimes the things that may or may not be true are the things that a man needs to believe in the most.... Doesn't matter if it's true or not. [A] man should believe in those things, because those are the things worth believing in."
  (*Secondhand Lions*)

THE THIRD PLOT POINT

WHERE DOES IT BELONG?

75% of the way into your story.

THE THIRD PLOT Point is the low moment in your story. A minute ago, at the end of the Second Act, your protagonist seemed to have won a victory. Everything seemed to be going his way. He was getting the Truth figured out, and he seemed to have pushed the Lie to the back of his life. Even the antagonist appeared to be at his mercy.

Unfortunately, pushing that Lie to the back burner isn't good enough. Before the story can end, the Lie must reappear front and center and confront the protagonist head on. That's what the Third Plot Point is all about. This low moment—which is all the more crushing because it comes on the heels of a seeming victory—will *force* the character to stop deceiving himself about the Lie. He can't evade it anymore. He can't pretend it away. He must confront it once and for all—and either destroy it or be destroyed.

(For more information about the Third Plot Point in a Positive Change Arc, see Chapter 11 in *Creating Character Arcs*.)

What Third Plot Point crisis will force your protagonist to a low moment in both the

inner and outer conflicts? _____

_____

_____

_____.

EXAMPLES:

*   Thor's brother Loki attempts to kill him by sending a Destroyer to attack the innocent New Mexican town in which Thor has been living and making friends.
    (*Thor*)

- On her wedding day, Jane discovers Rochester is already married to a madwoman he keeps locked in the attic.
  (*Jane Eyre*)

- After Andy's other toys falsely believe Woody killed Buzz and then refuse to help him escape the evil neighbor kid Sid's house, Woody watches helplessly as a despondent Buzz is strapped to Sid's rocket.
  (*Toy Story*)

What does the antagonistic force do to enact the reversal that occurs at the Third Plot

Point? _____

_____.

How could your antagonist utilize an understanding of your protagonist's Lie-

empowered weakness to gain the upper hand?_____

_____

_____.

How will your protagonist's main plot goal be dramatically endangered as a result?

_____

_____.

How does the Third Plot Point finally cause the character to make a choice between the

Thing She Wants and the Thing She Needs by forcing her to sacrifice one or the

other? _____

_____.

How can you make the consequences of this choice (whether the character chooses the Lie or the Truth) as painful as possible? _____

_____

_____

_____.

How can you make it as easy and pleasant as possible for the character to choose the Lie and the Thing She Wants—making it all the harder for her reject it? _

_____

_____

_____.

What will finally prompt the character to do the right thing in recognizing the true horror of the Lie and rejecting the Thing She Wants in favor of the Truth and the Thing She Needs? _____

_____

_____.

What irretrievable action will your character take in burning her bridges and proving her choice of the Truth? _____

_____

_____.

EXAMPLE:

- Jane realizes she can only remain with Rochester if she's willing to sacrifice her spiritual and moral freedom by becoming his mistress. She decides the price for being loved is too high—and flees Thornfield Hall.

How can you cast the pall of death over the Third Plot Point by featuring it either

literally or symbolically? _____

_____

_____

_____.

EXAMPLE:

- Scrooge is visited by the reaper-like Ghost of Christmas Future who reveals to him his own future death, as well as that of Tiny Tim. (*A Christmas Carol*)

THE FIRST HALF OF THE THIRD ACT

WHERE DOES IT BELONG?

From the 75% mark to the 88% mark in your story.

O N ITS EXTERIOR, the beginning of the Third Act is all about your character's scrambling to regain his balance before he faces the antagonist in the Climax. But within your character's interior, the Third Act is all about his figuring out if he *really* wants to serve the Truth after all. Is it worth the price he's just paid at the Third Plot Point? If he's ever going to return to his life of "safety" in the Lie, this is going to be his last chance.

(For more information about the First Half of the Third Act in a Positive Change Arc, see Chapter 12 in *Creating Character Arcs*.)

How can you up the stakes after the Third Plot Point by compounding your character's

misery? _____

_____

_____.

Will the character have reason to at least momentarily regret his decision to embrace

the Truth (e.g., he feels maybe he did the *right* thing, but not the *smart* thing)? _____

_____.

How will your character gain mastery over his pain and rise with the conviction that

he made the right choice and that the Thing He Needs is worth the price? _____

_____

_____.

EXAMPLE:

- Matt is tremendously uncomfortable with his Third Plot Point decision to leave behind the violence of the football firms and abandon his "mates" just as they're headed off to fight the opposing firm that tried to kill his brother-in-law. He knows he's in over his head this time, and he knows he needs to get his sister and nephew to safety, but he can't help feeling like he's walking away when he should be fighting. Still, he gets in the car and starts driving to the airport.
  (*Green Street Hooligans*)

Even after your character fully claims the Truth, how can you keep him off-balance

by nudging him with reflexive Lie-inspired doubts? _____

_____

_____

_____.

How will the doubts in this section keep your character from being either

completely fulfilled or completely effective in his new Truth-driven life? _____

_____

_____

_____.

EXAMPLE:

- After agreeing with "the fam" that it would be best for Leo if Bob went back to New York City, Bob bravely marches out into the dark forest. Even though he's proven his sanity over and over throughout the second half of the story, he finds himself riddled with doubts. He surrenders to his fear and runs, screaming, back to the lake house.
  (*What About Bob?*)

How is your character different in the Third Act from who he was in the First Act?

_____

_____.

How can you demonstrate this by giving your protagonist the opportunity to

symbolically reject the temptation of the Lie in a physical way? _____

_____

_____

_____.

EXAMPLE:

- The protagonist—an image consultant who was previously an arro-gant jerk—humbly seeks the counsel of a local news anchor, whom he memorably snubbed in the First Act.
  (*The Kid*)

- Dr. Grant demonstrates his newfound affection for the children when he reassures them before leaving them in (what he believes is) the safety of the main lobby. He pats down Tim's static hair and teases, "Big Tim, the human piece of toast"—something he would never have contemplated in the beginning of the story.
  (*Jurassic Park*)

Prior to the Climax, how can you use a minor character (*other* than the main antagonist)

to try to tempt the protagonist away from the Truth by insisting his new paradigm is un-

wise? _____

_____

_____.

- Just before the Climax (in which she will flee back to Thornfield, fearing for Rochester's life), Jane is subjected to a brutal attack upon her new Truth. Her cousin St. John Rivers insists her new Truth is a selfish and worthless pursuit. He uses her own former beliefs against her to try to convince her she can only live a worthwhile life if she enters a loveless marriage with him and joins him as a missionary in India. (*Jane Eyre*)

Which of the following characters will you use for this renewed attack?

□ Minor antagonist, named: _____.

□ Skeptical or fearful ally, named: _____.

□ Protagonist's inner doubts.

□ Other: _____.

How will this attack specifically target the protagonist's own remaining doubts

about his new Truth? _____

_____

_____

_____.

How will the Lie be presented in the most attractive terms possible? _____

_____

_____

_____.

How will the protagonist overcome his temptation and embrace his new Truth

even more strongly? _____

_____

_____.

Decide where to place this Renewed Attack by circling all of the following that best apply to your story:

    ☒ The exterior conflict with your main antagonistic force is closely related to the protagonist's internal conflict.

    ☑ The protagonist's ability to defeat the antagonistic force depends entirely on his full and final rejection of the Lie.

    ☒ The Climax will lack tension and meaning if the character is already secure in his Truth.

    ☑ The Climax will be too "busy" to contain both the character's inner and outer victories at the same time.

    ☑ Including the necessary internal narrative to complete your character's arc would slow down the external action of the Climax.

    ☑ The character would not be able to realistically defeat the antagonistic force in the Climax if he were not *entering* the confrontation already secure in the Truth.

    ☑ The Climax works best if it is an outer demonstration of the character's new Truth.

    ☒ The Climax works best if it is the character's final test in overcoming the Lie.

If you have circled more ☑ marks, you should plan to time your Renewed Attack *before* the Climax.

If you have circled more ☒ marks, you should plan to time your Renewed Attack to take place *during* the Climax.

THE CLIMAX

WHERE DOES IT BELONG?

From the 88% mark to the 98% mark in your story.

THE CLIMAX IS where your character proves once and for all he is a changed person. Your readers have witnessed his evolution. They've seen him get shaken up when he was kicked out of his Normal World. They watched his desperate reactions as he tried to regain his footing in the First Half of the Second Act. They saw his revelation at the Midpoint, and his subsequent transition away from his Lie and toward the Truth. They saw him act on the Truth at the Third Plot Point—and pay the price for doing so.

Now, approximately halfway through the Third Act, the conflict has revved to the point where a confrontation *must* happen between the protagonist and the antagonistic force. If the protagonist is to have any chance of winning that conflict, he must prove he is able to stick with the Truth for the long haul. If he can't gather all the lessons he's learned throughout the story and hang onto them now, when the pressure is greatest, then all will be lost forever.

(For more information about the Climax in a Positive Change Arc, see Chapter 13 in *Creating Character Arcs*.)

How has your character recently proven *before* the Climax that she is a changed person? _____

_____.

What form will the final confrontation between the protagonist and the antagonistic

force take? _____

_____

_____

_____.

- Naval battle.
  (*Master and Commander*)

- Horse race.
  (*The Reivers*)

- Filibuster.
  (*Mr. Smith Goes to Washington*)

Where will your Climax take place? _____.

How does this setting symbolically emphasize the central conflict and the

theme? _____.

How does this setting physically or emotionally make the confrontation with

the antagonist more difficult? _____

_____.

How is the nature of the final climactic confrontation perfectly suited to provide the

final test for your protagonist's new Truth, absolutely proving her devotion to it?

_____

_____.

How will the antagonistic force attempt to use the character's Lie against her one

last time—and fail? _____

_____

_____

_____.

How will the protagonist use her new Truth to overcome the antagonistic force and remove the last obstacle between herself and her main plot goal?

_____

_____

_____.

What one moment have readers been waiting for since the beginning of the story? _

_____.

EXAMPLES:

- The kiss between the romantic leads.
  (*North & South*)

- The White Witch's death.
  (*The Lion, the Witch, and the Wardrobe*)

- The return of the hero's memory.
  (*Random Harvest*)

How can you deliver this moment? _____

_____

_____.

Which of the following best describes your character's climactic relationship to the Thing He Wants?

☐ The character is now so fulfilled in the Thing He Needs that he no longer desires the Thing He Wants and can walk away from it.

EXAMPLE:

- Jockey Mi Taylor has gained self-respect and no longer wants to steal from the Browns or trade off his father's name.
  (*National Velvet*)

☐ The character still desires the Thing She Wants, but she is now strong enough to reject it, understanding it's impossible for her to possess both it and the Thing She Needs.

EXAMPLE:

- Peter Parker rejects the opportunity for a relationship with Mary Jane, because he knows it's the only way to protect her. (*Spider-Man*)

☐ The character's reasons for pursuing the Thing He Wants have changed, so that obtaining it now feels bittersweet.

EXAMPLE:

- Russ Duritz achieves his goal of getting rid of his younger self (having now come to peace with the "kid in himself"), only to miss having him around. (*The Kid*)

☐ The character gains and embraces the Thing She Wants, but only because she has first learned to embrace the Thing She Needs.

EXAMPLE:

- Emma Woodhouse gets to marry her true love Mr. Knightley, but only because she has finally overcome her selfishness and conceit. (*Emma*)

THE RESOLUTION

WHERE DOES IT BELONG?

From the 98% mark to the 100% mark in your story.

THIS IMPORTANT ENDING scene(s) is necessary to bookend your opening scene. In the beginning of your story, you showed your character living in his Normal World, as shaped by the Lie. In the Resolution, you get to show readers the *new* Normal World that has been built by the character's hard-won Truth.

Think of this final scene as a reward. Readers laughed, cried, ached, and triumphed right alongside your character. Now they want a glimpse of the new and improved life your character is going to live after he rides off into the sunset.

(For more information about the Resolution in a Positive Change Arc, see Chapter 14 in *Creating Character Arcs*.)

Now that the main conflict has been resolved, what is your character planning to do

next? _____

_____.

How will this choice for a new life contrast the choices the character would have made

back in the first chapter? _____

_____

_____.

EXAMPLE:

- In a scene that closely mirrors the opening one, a newly empowered Walter marches down the road to his uncles' farm, greets the previously fearsome dogs and pig, and tells his uncles they must see him through college.
(*Secondhand Lions*)

Name three ways you can contrast the Normal World from the beginning of the story with the new normal.

1. _____.

2. _____.

3. _____.

If it is possible for you to *physically* return your character to the Normal World,

how can you contrast the character's new self with the old world? _____

_____

_____

_____

_____.

EXAMPLE:

- When Amy Dorrit returns to visit the Marshalsea Prison after her father's death in Venice, she is a different person, from top to toe, which is visually obvious in the contrast between the dreary prison and the rich clothing she now wears.
  (*Little Dorrit*)

How will your Resolution answer the Thematic Question you asked in the first chap-

ter? _____

_____

_____

_____.

EXAMPLE:

- **Thematic Question:** Will Peter Parker learn to wield his great power with equally great responsibility?

- **Thematic Answer:** Yes: he is willing to sacrifice the one thing he wants most—the love of Mary Jane Watson—in order to be responsible and protect her.
(*Spider-Man*)

How can you visually *show* the character's new thematic Truth without slapping

readers in the face with the "moral of the story"? _____

_____

_____

_____.

EXAMPLE:

- The previously arrogant Thor apologizes to his father and in so doing blatantly answers the Thematic Question: "I have much to learn. I know that now."
(*Thor*)

How will your final scene be an upbeat one that demonstrates the hope of a new and

better day dawning for the protagonist? _____

_____

_____

_____

_____.

CREATIVE EXERCISE:

Most characters demonstrate multiple thematically related Lies and Truths. After you have mapped out your protagonist's main arc from Lie to Truth, see if you can identify any Truths he already possesses and that perhaps allow him to aid minor characters in overcoming their own related Lies.

SOMETHING TO THINK ABOUT:

1. Will the First Plot Point *seem* favorable? If so, how will the complications turn out to be worse than the protagonist expected?
2. What minor character can offer advice or exemplary behavior to help mentor your protagonist?
3. How does the contrast between the simultaneously held Lie and Truth evolve your character's inner conflict?
4. How is the revelation at the Midpoint allowing your character to see the conflict in a new light?

RESOURCES:

- "Your Book's Inciting Event: It's Not What You Think It Is," helpingwriters-becomeauthors.com/your-books-inciting-event-its-not-what-you-think-it-is
- "Never Confuse the Key Event and the First Plot Point in Your Book Again!," helpingwritersbecomeauthors.com/never-confuse-the-key-event-and-the-first-plot-point-in-your-book-again
- "What Are Pinch Points? And How Can They Make Your Book Easier to Write?," helpingwritersbecomeauthors.com/what-are-pinch-points-and-how-can-they-make-your-book-easier-to-write
- "How to Transform Your Story With a Moment of Truth," helpingwritersbecomeauthors.com/moment-of-truth/
- "Want Readers to Adore Your Book? Learn How to Ace Your Climactic Moment," helpingwritersbecomeauthors.com/want-readers-to-adore-your-book-learn-how-to-ace-your-climactic-moment

2
THE FLAT ARC

CHARACTER BELIEVES TRUTH > MAINTAINS TRUTH >
USES TRUTH TO OVERCOME WORLD'S LIE

NEXT TO THE Positive Change Arc, the Flat Arc is the most popular story-line. Also called the "testing arc," the Flat Arc is about a character who does *not* change. He already has the Truth figured out in the beginning of the story, and he uses that Truth to overcome various external tests.

The Flat-arc protagonist will be confronted with tremendous opposition. He will at times be shaken. His commitment to the Truth will be tested to the breaking point—but he will never step away from it.

Like the Change Arcs, the Flat Arc is also a story of change. The difference is that the Flat-Arc protagonist is the one changing the world *around* him, rather than the world changing the character, as we find in Change-Arc protagonists.

As you will see, many of the principles of the Positive Change Arc remain true for the Flat Arc, but with some significant variations.

FLAT ARC

CHARACTER BELIEVES TRUTH >
MAINTAINS TRUTH >
USES TRUTH TO OVERCOME
WORLD'S LIE

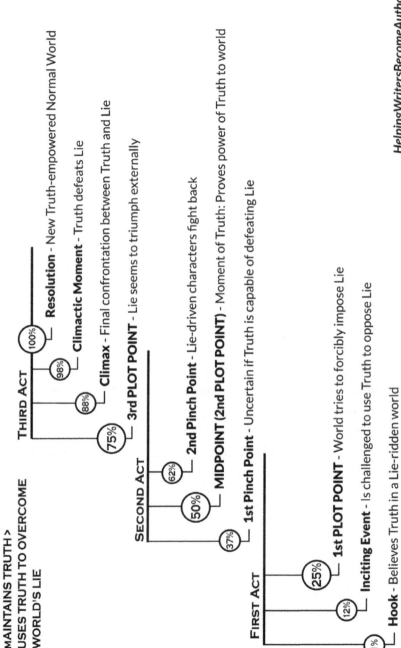

FIRST ACT

1% — **Hook** - Believes Truth in a Lie-ridden world

12% — **Inciting Event** - Is challenged to use Truth to oppose Lie

25% — **1st PLOT POINT** - World tries to forcibly impose Lie

SECOND ACT

37% — **1st Pinch Point** - Uncertain if Truth is capable of defeating Lie

50% — **MIDPOINT (2nd PLOT POINT)** - Moment of Truth: Proves power of Truth to world

62% — **2nd Pinch Point** - Lie-driven characters fight back

THIRD ACT

75% — **3rd PLOT POINT** - Lie seems to triumph externally

88% — **Climax** - Final confrontation between Truth and Lie

98% — **Climactic Moment** - Truth defeats Lie

100% — **Resolution** - New Truth-empowered Normal World

THE TRUTH YOUR CHARACTER BELIEVES

THE FLAT ARC is about the *Truth* the Character Believes. The protagonist already has a handle on the Truth, and he will use that Truth to overcome the challenges of the plot—and, probably, to transform a Lie-burdened world.

(For more information about the Truth Your Character Believes in a Flat Arc, see Chapter 15 in *Creating Character Arcs*.)

Write down four possible variations of the Truth Your Character Believes. Each one should be a specific belief, stated in one short sentence.

EXAMPLES:

- Society should be based on trust and compassion rather than fear and sadism.
  (*The Hunger Games*)

- A sensible approach to life and love will bear greater fruits than wild emotional abandon.
  (*Sense & Sensibility*)

- Justice is about harmony.
  (*Batman Begins*)

Truth #1: _____

_____.

Truth #2: _____

_____.

Truth #3: _____

_____.

Truth #4: _____

_____.

Which of these four Truths will be the primary Truth for your story? Which one best influences your plot and theme?

☐ Truth #1
☐ Truth #2
☐ Truth #3
☐ Truth #4

What major Lie—as represented by the antagonistic force—will stand in opposition

to your protagonist's Truth? _____

_____

_____

_____

_____

_____

_____

_____.

Write down four variations of this Lie (or "sub-Lies") that can be present in the lives of four of your minor characters.

Sub-Lie   **Minor Character**

1. _____   1. _____

2. _____   2. _____

3. _____   3. _____

4. _____   4. _____

Does your protagonist have a Ghost in her backstory? If so, how has the Truth already helped her find closure for this wound? _____

_____

_____

_____

_____

_____

_____

_____.

Will readers need to explicitly understand the Ghost in order for the rest of the story to make sense?

    ☐ Yes
    ☐ No

This Ghost will best be shared with readers how?

    ☐ As a mystery (teased in the beginning and revealed later at an important turning point in the plot)

    ☐ Dramatized at the beginning of the First Act

    ☐ Not shared at all

THE NORMAL WORLD

JUST AS IN the Positive Change Arc, the Normal World in which a Flat-Arc story opens will be a symbol, either of what the protagonist is fighting to protect or what he's fighting to overcome. It sets the stage for the story to follow. (For more information about the Normal World in a Flat Arc, see Chapter 15 in *Creating Character Arcs*.)

Start by determining what type of Normal World will best set up your character's arc. Which of the following will work best?

☐ Normal World is a good place that represents the protagonist's Truth.

EXAMPLE:

- Elinor Dashwood's Normal World on her father's estate at Norland Park provides her and her family a comfortable, orderly, and safe existence—until her father dies and the family is thrust out by a careless half-brother.
  (*Sense & Sensibility*)

How might you create this type of Normal World for your story? _____

_____

_____

_____

_____.

Will this Normal World be destroyed at the First Plot Point or will the protagonist be

forced to journey away from it to protect it? How will this occur? _____

_____

_____

_____.

☐   Normal World is a less-than-satisfactory place cursed by a great Lie.

EXAMPLE:

• Ginger and her friends are imprisoned in a stalag-like chicken farm—
  against which Ginger fights continually, at great risk to her own life,
  insisting she will "die free or die trying."
  (*Chicken Run*)

How might you create this type of Normal World for your story? _____

_____

_____

_____

_____.

How will the protagonist use his Truth to eventually destroy or escape this destruc-

tive Normal World and build a better one in its place? _____

_____

_____

_____

_____.

Describe the physical setting of the Normal World (e.g., Chicago or Mars): _____

_____

_____

_____.

How is the Lie reflected in your character's exterior world and/or how can the exterior world be a metaphor for the Truth your protagonist will fight to protect? _____

_____

_____

_____.

EXAMPLE:

- Katniss lives in a stark Normal World where she remains in constant fear of the government as she struggles to feed and protect her mother and sister.
(*The Hunger Games*)

- Bruce Wayne's Normal World is a glittering façade of wealth that hides the rotten epicenter of Gotham's corruption.
(*Batman Begins*)

How will the Normal World visibly prove to readers (*show* them) the world's "before"

state at the beginning of the story? _____

_____

_____.

What setting for the Normal World provides the most logical backstory for *why* your

minor characters believe the Lie? _____

_____.

What has kept your protagonist from leaving the Normal World before now? _____

_____

_____.

Why has your protagonist not been spurred by his Truth to overcome the Lie before

now? _____

_____.

How will the Normal World contrast with the Adventure World that will follow in the

next two acts? _____

_____

_____.

Which of the following will best describe the main conflict's Adventure World of your story's Second Act?

☐   A dramatically new and different setting.

EXAMPLE:

- Katniss leaves District 12 to compete in the Hunger Games at Capitol City.
  (*The Hunger Games*)

☐   The same physical setting as the Normal World, with only facets of the world changing.

EXAMPLE:

- Maximus's Normal World of Rome doesn't change its physical setting, but morphs into the Adventure World when Commodus becomes emperor and Maximus becomes a slave.
  (*Gladiator*)

THE CHARACTERISTIC MOMENT

BEFORE YOU CAN craft the perfect Characteristic Moment, you must first know something about your protagonist. Answer the following questions for starters (and for a full character interview, see my books *Outlining Your Novel* and the *Outlining Your Novel Workbook*).

What is your character's name? _____.

How old is your character? _____.

Of what nationality is your character? _____.

What is your character's occupation or primary identity (e.g., stay-at-home mom, rebel

Soldier)? _____

_____.

Does the character have any important physical characteristics (e.g., a limp, green

scales)? _____

_____.

Name three prevailing aspects of the character's personality (e.g., kindness, quick temper, wit):

     1. _____.

     2. _____.

     3. _____.

What *one* important personality trait, virtue, or skill best sums up your character? ____

_____.

How can you dramatize this aspect of your character to its fullest extent? ___

_____

_____.

How can you dramatize this aspect in a way that also introduces the plot? ___

_____

_____.

What do you want readers to find most sympathetic and/or interesting about this

character? _____

_____.

How can you dramatize this aspect of your character in an opening scene? __

_____

_____.

What is your character's overall story goal? _____

_____

_____

_____.

How can you set up this goal or show the coming need for it in an opening

scene? _____

_____.

In your first chapter, how can you dramatize the contrast between your Truth-ful-filled protagonist and the Lie-ridden characters around him? _____

_____

_____

_____.

What is your character's scene goal in the opening chapter? _____

_____

_____.

How will you dramatize this scene goal right from the start of your opening scene? _____

_____.

How will the character's pursuit of this goal meet with an obvious obstacle (i.e., conflict)? _____

_____

_____.

How will this goal move the plot, either by immediately causing consequences or setting them up for later? _____

_____

_____.

How can any of the above help you demonstrate, or at least hint at, your character's

Truth? _____

_____ .

If appropriate, how can you reveal or at least hint at your character's Ghost? _____

_____

_____ .

How can you craft the above elements to make your protagonist immediately appeal-

ing to readers (e.g., what's keeping them from looking away?)? _____

_____

_____

_____ .

Which of your character's strengths can you show readers right away? _____

_____

_____

_____ .

Which of your character's pertinent weaknesses can you show readers right away? __

_____

_____

_____ .

List events or activities you can use in your opening chapter to dramatize all the above. Try to think of "big" moments that are unique, visually engaging, and keep the characters in motion.

1. _____.

2. _____.

3. _____.

4. _____.

5. _____.

Write a summary of your opening chapter and how you will introduce your character in

a memorable and engaging Characteristic Moment: _____

_____

_____

_____

_____

_____

_____

_____

_____

_____.

Which of the following does your Characteristic Moment accomplish?

- ☐ Introduce character.
- ☐ Reveal character's name.
- ☐ Indicate character's gender.
- ☐ Indicate character's age group.
- ☐ Indicate character's nationality.
- ☐ Indicate character's occupation/main identity.
- ☐ Indicate any important physical characteristics.
- ☐ Indicate character's role in the story (i.e., protagonist).
- ☐ Demonstrate prevailing aspect of personality.
- ☐ Hook readers' sympathy and/or interest.
- ☐ Show character's scene goal.
- ☐ Indicate character's story goal.
- ☐ Demonstrate (or at least hint at) character's Truth.
- ☐ Move the plot directly or through foreshadowing.

If you're unable to combine most of the above elements into one scene, answer whether it would work better to divide the necessary characteristic elements into two or more scenes. _____

_____

_____

_____

_____.

THE FIRST ACT

WHERE DOES IT BELONG?

From the 1% mark to the 25% mark in your story.

WITHIN THE FIRST quarter of a Flat-Arc story, your primary responsibility will be setting the stage for the coming conflict. You must introduce the important characters and their respective alignments with either the Truth or the Lie. Just as in a Positive Change Arc, this is the time to lavish some extra attention on the Lie, because within the Lie is always where we discover what is at stake for the protagonist. What horrible things will happen to him and his world if the Lie isn't overthrown?

(For more information about the First Act in a Flat Arc, see Chapter 15 in *Creating Character Arcs*.)

How will you reinforce/dramatize the protagonist's Truth? _____

_____

_____

_____.

EXAMPLE:

- Katniss is introduced in a Characteristic Moment of caring for her family by providing food for them—which is then reinforced in the Inciting Event when she sacrifices herself to take her sister's place in the Reaping.
  (*The Hunger Games*)

How will you introduce the Lie that exists in the world and characters around him? _

_____

_____

_____

_____.

How can you demonstrate what is at stake for the protagonist to lose if she is not eventually able to overcome or escape the Lie in the world around her? _____

_____

_____

_____.

Is the character immediately cognizant of the Lie in the world?

☐ Yes
☐ No

If not, how will he grow into an awareness of its darkness and the necessity of resisting it over the course of the First Act? _____

_____

_____.

If the character is aware of the Lie, why has he resisted engaging with it up to this point? _____

_____

_____.

Name three ways you will continue to reinforce the world's Lie or introduce more of its facets throughout the First Act:

1. _____.

2. _____.

3. _____.

What specific quality will be intrinsic to your character's ability to fight the Lie? ____

_____.

     Even if this trait isn't yet fully developed, how can you hint right from the begin-

ning that the seed is there? _____

_____

_____.

What Inciting Event will be the Call to Adventure that first brushes your character against

the main conflict? _____

_____

_____

_____.

EXAMPLE:

- Steve Rogers learns about SHIELD's plan to "eliminate" threats before they manifest.
  (*Captain America: The Winter Soldier*)

How will this Inciting Event set up the character's entry into the Adventure World of the

main conflict in the Second Act? _____

_____

_____.

Does the Inciting Event initially seem:

     ☐ a good thing.

     ☐ a bad thing.

How will the Call to Adventure initially be met with resistance or refusal? _____

_____

_____

_____

_____.

EXAMPLE:

- Steve knows he can't maintain his Truth if he remains in SHIELD, but instead of immediately determining to fight them, he spends the bulk of the First Act contemplating simply walking away.

Will the protagonist be the one to initially reject the Call to Adventure, or will some

one else try to reject it for him? _____.

How long will it take the protagonist to stop resisting?

☐ Entire rest of the First Act up to the First Plot Point.

☐ Shorter period ending with what event _____.

How does the Inciting Event change the protagonist's awareness of and ability to

coexist with the Lie, in however small or subconscious a way? _____

_____

_____

_____

_____.

What will the protagonist decide to *do* about the Call to Adventure at the Inciting

Event? _____

_____

_____

_____

_____.

EXAMPLE:
- After Mattie Ross waylays Rooster Cogburn, the "meanest" marshal, outside the courthouse, it's supporting character Rooster who initially rejects the Call to Adventure by refusing to help her bring her father's murderer to justice. Mattie, however, persists in tracking him down at the courthouse the next day, accompanying him home to dinner, and eventually convincing him to give in to her proposition. (*True Grit*)

THE FIRST PLOT POINT

WHERE DOES IT BELONG?

25% of the way into your story.

THIS MAJOR SCENE is the first turning point in your story. It marks the end of the First Act and the beginning of the Second. It's the first "doorway" through which your character must walk. He will leave the Normal World of the First Act and irrevocably enter the new "adventure" world of the story.

The First Plot Point functions very similarly in both Change and Flat Arcs. It will be a major (probably catastrophic) event that will upend your character's world and force him into a reaction that will pit his personal Truth directly against the world's Lie.

(For more information about the First Plot Point in a Flat Arc, see Chapter 16 in *Creating Character Arcs*.)

What event occurs at the end of the First Act that causes your character to leave

the Normal World and irreversibly engage with the main conflict? _____

_____

_____

_____.

EXAMPLES:

- Katniss arrives squarely in enemy territory—Capitol City—where she will be participating in the gladiatorial Hunger Games.
  (*The Hunger Games*)

- Elinor and her family leave their home in Norland Park and arrive at the Devonshire cottage where they must now live.
  (*Sense & Sensibility*)

- After destroying Ra's al Ghul's fortress, Bruce returns to Gotham after a seven-year absence to begin planning his Batman persona.
  (*Batman Begins*)

In what way might this event be surprising even after the Inciting Event? _____

_____

_____

_____.

Which of the following best describes your First Plot Point?

☐   A seemingly positive opportunity.

EXAMPLE:

- Ginger discovers an opportunity for escape when circus performer Rocky crash lands inside the pen.
  (*Chicken Run*)

☐   Something disastrous.

EXAMPLE:

- Maximus's family is murdered and he is enslaved as a gladiator.
  (*Gladiator*)

What decision on your character's part led him right up to the First Plot Point,

making him at least partially responsible for what happens? _____

_____

_____.

EXAMPLES:

- Katniss volunteered to take her sister's place in the Games.
- Elinor chooses the Devonshire cottage in order to escape her cruel sister-in-law.
- Bruce refuses to act as executioner at R'as al Ghul's bidding and instead destroys the League of Shadows fortress.

Which of the following best describes your First Plot Point?

☐ It destroys the Normal World, leaving the protagonist no choice but to move on.

EXAMPLE:

- The old Rome Maximus knew under Emperor Marcus Aurelius disappears upon his murder.

☐ It physically removes the protagonist from the Normal World.

EXAMPLE:

- Katniss is forcibly taken to the Capitol.

☐ It warps the Normal World, forcing the protagonist to adapt to new ways of surviving within it.

EXAMPLE:

- After SHIELD director Nick Fury is shot by his own people, Steve must go on the run to discover what happened.
  (*Captain America: The Winter Soldier*)

Which best describes your protagonist's reaction to the First Plot Point?

☐ Enthusiasm—she wants to enter the conflict of the Second Act.

☐ Resistance—she must be forced to enter the conflict of the Second Act.

How will the First Plot Point force your character into a reaction that directly pits his

personal Truth against the world's Lie? _____

_____.

Why do the events of the First Plot Point convince him his First-Act tactics (of

avoiding the conflict or trying more diplomatic approaches) are no longer plau-

sible?_____

_____.

What definitive action will he take to move forward into the Adventure World of

the main conflict? _____

_____.

Which will the character be trying to do?

☐ Restore the old normal of a Truth-based Normal World.

How: _____.

☐ Find a new normal by destroying the Lie-based Normal World.

How: _____.

Name three new physical needs that must be met in the aftermath of the First Plot Point:

1. _____.

2. _____.

3. _____.

What definitive new plot goal will the character now adopt (something quantifiable,

based on maintaining or reclaiming the Truth)? _____

_____

_____.

Do you want the character to ultimately achieve this goal?

☐ Yes.
How? _____.

☐ No.
How? _____.

THE FIRST HALF OF THE SECOND ACT

WHERE DOES IT BELONG?

From the 25% mark to the 50% mark in your story.

IN CONTRAST TO the Positive Change Arc, the Flat-Arc character is going to spend the First Half of the Second Act getting punished for believing the Truth. Everyone around him will try to convince him he's an idiot for opposing the Lie. His devotion to the Truth must be tested, and for these tests to have any teeth, the character *must* become less than certain about the Truth. He needs to seriously consider whether he's actually following the Truth after all. Could it be that he's wrong and everyone else is right? Maybe the Truth is really a Lie, and the Lie is really the Truth! For anywhere from a few moments to a few scenes, he's not quite certain what to believe. But he never fully turns his back on the Truth.

(For more information about the First Half of the Second Act in a Flat Arc, see Chapter 16 in *Creating Character Arcs*.)

What "tools" will your character begin to receive that offer hints for how to start

opposing the antagonist's Lie? _____

_____

_____

_____

_____

_____.

EXAMPLE:

- Katniss is trained in how to survive the games.
  (*The Hunger Games*)

How can your protagonist *show* other characters the Truth, rather than just *telling* her about it? _____

_____

_____

_____.

How is your protagonist feeling slightly out of place within the new Adventure World of the Second Act? _____

_____

_____.

What Truth-based actions is the protagonist still trying to use to reach his goals? ____

_____

_____

_____.

How are other Lie-driven characters opposing the character's Truth-based actions and "punishing" him for trying to use them? _____

_____

_____.

EXAMPLE:

- As Steve begins to investigate the corruption at SHIELD's heart, the agency brands him a fugitive and tries to kill him.
  (*Captain America: The Winter Soldier*)

How is the punishment the protagonist is enduring causing him to question

whether his Truth really is true? _____

_____

_____.

How can you tempt the character with the promise of how great life seems to be

"if only he would come over to the Lie"? _____

_____

_____.

THE MIDPOINT

WHERE DOES IT BELONG?

50% of the way into your story.

THE MIDPOINT IS your story's centerpiece. It's a reversal caused by an important revelation. Something happens that provides the protagonist with new information. Suddenly, all the questions from the first half begin to find answers. He figures out what the antagonistic force is *really* up to and/or capable of, and he sees for the first time how corrupted and powerful the Lie really is.

Just as in the Positive Change Arc, the Midpoint and its revelations must include a Moment of Truth. The difference here is that this redemptive moment of insight and new resolve isn't offered *to* the protagonist. Instead, the protagonist is the one who (figuratively or literally) offers the Truth to the world around him. Allies who previously resisted the Truth (and who will be, essentially, following Positive Change Arcs of their own) will begin to see the light. Enemies (who are following Negative Change Arcs) will scoff and toss the Truth's offered grace right back into the protagonist's face.

(For more information about the Midpoint in a Flat Arc, see Chapter 16 in *Creating Character Arcs*.)

What is your story's Midpoint event? _____

_____.

EXAMPLES:

- Katniss is saved from the tracker-jacker attack by fellow tribute Peeta, prompting her to reject any notion of killing him in order to win the game.
  (*The Hunger Games*)

- Elinor's sister Marianne is abandoned without explanation by her suitor Willoughby.
  (*Sense & Sensibility*)

- Bruce destroys gang lord Carmine Falcone's drug operation and reveals his "sign" to the city.
  (*Batman Begins*)

What can you do to make this centerpiece scene as "big" as possible? _____

_____

_____

_____

_____.

How will the external events of the Midpoint prompt a "Moment of Truth," which

the protagonist is able to (figuratively or literally) offer the world around him? _____

_____

_____

_____

_____.

Example:

- Steve uncovers the full extent of SHIELD's corruption and "offers" that Truth to the change-arc character Natasha Romanov, who begins to demonstrate how Steve's views are evolving her own mercenary mindset.
  (*Captain America: The Winter Soldier*)

How will the Moment of Truth prompt minor characters to turn away from the

effects of the Lie in their lives? _____

_____

_____

_____.

Name four ways in which the protagonist's Truth is beginning to affect other characters:

Character   **Changed How**

1. _____   1. _____

2. _____   2. _____

3. _____   3. _____

4. _____   4. _____

How will a plot-related realization at the Midpoint help the character better under

stand the true nature of the antagonist's Lie (and thus be better equipped to conquer

it)? _____

_____

_____

_____

_____.

How will the events of the Midpoint act as a swivel between the two halves of your

story—shifting your character out of uninformed reaction and into educated action?

_____

_____

_____

_____.

THE SECOND HALF OF THE SECOND ACT

WHERE DOES IT BELONG?

From the 50% mark to the 75% mark in your story.

THE MIDPOINT HAS changed everything for the protagonist. His doubts have been, for the most part, swept aside. He knows what he's up against, and he knows what he has to do to confront the Lie. It's a long shot, of course, but he's willing to die trying if he has to.

Now that the protagonist has seen the true power of the Lie, he's also seen its weakness (even if it's just a tiny one), and he's determined to exploit it. His aggressive actions in this section will dramatically affect the world around him. Even as the Lie bears down hard, the world is beginning to awaken to the true horror of the belief it's been cultivating all story long. Supporting characters are starting to rally to the protagonist's cause, and the antagonistic force is starting to sweat. The Second Act will end with what seems a definitive victory for the protagonist—but it's really just the setup for what will be his greatest defeat yet at the Third Plot Point.

(For more information about the Second Half of the Second Act in a Flat Arc, see Chapter 16 in *Creating Character Arcs*.)

How is the character acting on her Midpoint revelation about the conflict? _____

_____

_____

_____.

What new "tools" did the Moment of Truth provide your character that will allow him to

make better progress toward overcoming the antagonistic force? _____

_____

_____.

What obstacles will the antagonistic force still be putting in his way? _____

_____

_____

_____.

EXAMPLE:

- After Maximus reveals himself to Emperor Commodus at the Midpoint and vows to dethrone him, Commodus makes every attempt to have Maximus killed in the Coliseum.
  (*Gladiator*)

How is the Lie still a grave threat in the world around the protagonist? _____

_____

_____

_____

_____.

EXAMPLE:

- Despite Elinor's pleas for sensibleness, Marianne's hysteria increases as she learns her passion for Willoughby was ill-founded—he was a rake who abandoned her to marry an heiress after fathering a child by still another woman.
  (*Sense & Sensibility*)

How is the world around the protagonist caught between the Lie and the Truth? ____

_____

_____

_____.

Are there some supporting characters who might now start acting more selflessly as they embrace the Truth more and more? _____

_____

_____.

Are there other supporting characters who might be stubbornly entrenching them selves even further into the Lie in resistance to the protagonist? _____

_____

_____.

EXAMPLE:

- Nathaniel's Truth that fighting to protect family is more important than fighting for a perfidious king completely changes his love interest Cora, while also impacting the stubborn soldier Duncan. However, Cora's father Colonel Munro entrenches himself even more deeply in the Lie, imprisoning Nathaniel and eventually losing his fort to the French and his life to the Indians.
  (*The Last of the Mohicans*)

Write down four scenes from the first half of the story in which your supporting characters resisted your protagonist's Truth. Then brainstorm four scenes you can include in the second half that will contrast the earlier scenes by showing how your protagonist has started to inspire a new understanding of the Truth in the world around him.

"Before" Scenes

1. _____

2. _____

3. _____

4. _____

"After" Scenes

1. _____

2. _____

3. _____

4. _____

EXAMPLE:

- Before: The other chickens on the farm resist Ginger's harebrained escape ideas, insisting they want a third option to her "die free or die trying."

- After: They eagerly await their flying lessons and (when that proves a bust) industriously band together to build a plane.
(*Chicken Run*)

At the end of the Second Act, how will the protagonist seem to gain a victory over

the Lie? _____

_____

_____

_____

_____.

EXAMPLE:

- Maximus manages to rally senators and soldiers to a secret plan to overthrow Commodus.

THE THIRD PLOT POINT

WHERE DOES IT BELONG?

75% of the way into your story.

AFTER WHAT SEEMED a great victory at the end of the Second Act, the tables will be completely turned on your protagonist and he'll be smacked back down into his most intense defeat yet. No matter what kind of arc your character is pursuing, the Third Plot Point is going to be his low moment—his breaking point. He's going to face down death, figuratively or literally, and he's going to come to terms with his fears, re-embrace the Truth, and rise with renewed determination and vigor.

In a Flat Arc, the protagonist won't actually doubt the Truth, but he will be brought to a point where he seriously doubts his *ability* to use the Truth to defeat the Lie. Make the Third Plot Point as personal as possible for your protagonist.

(For more information about the Third Plot Point in a Flat Arc, see Chapter 17 in *Creating Character Arcs*.)

What Third Plot Point crisis will force your protagonist to a personal low moment? _

_____

_____.

EXAMPLES:

- Katniss is gravely wounded and nearly dies after a battle at the Cornucopia.
  (*The Hunger Games*)

- On the heels of learning the truth about Willoughby's abandonment of Marianne, Elinor's own romantic hopes are slain when her own love Edward Ferrars is forced to announce his engagement to the horrible Lucy Steele.
  (*Sense & Sensibility*)

- R'as Al Ghul arrives to personally destroy Gotham—starting with Bruce and his family's manor. Bruce is wounded and barely escapes being trapped in the burning house.
  (*Batman Begins*)

What does the antagonistic force do to enact the reversal that occurs at the Third

Plot Point? _____

_____

_____

_____.

How could your antagonist utilize his full-blown Lie to gain the upper hand?

_____

_____

_____.

How will your protagonist's main plot goal be dramatically endangered as a

result? _____

_____

_____.

How does the Third Plot Point cause the protagonist to feel her cause is hopeless, that

she isn't capable of using the Truth to defeat the Lie? _____

_____

_____

_____.

How can you make this defeat as painful as possible? _____

_____

_____

_____.

How can you make the Lie seem as attractive as possible at this point? _____

_____

_____.

How will the character reinforce her commitment to the Truth—however

futile it seems—even in the midst of her pain? _____

_____

_____.

What irretrievable action will your character take in burning her bridges and prov-

ing her devotion to the Truth? _____

_____

_____

_____.

EXAMPLE:

- After Steve is sucker-punched with the realization that the enemy he's been fighting all along is really his long-lost best friend, he determines he must still go to battle against him.
(*Captain America: The Winter Soldier*)

How can you cast the pall of death over the Third Plot Point by featuring it either

literally or symbolically? _____

_____

_____

_____

_____

_____

_____

_____.

THE FIRST HALF OF THE THIRD ACT

WHERE DOES IT BELONG?

From the 75% mark to the 88% mark in your story.

THE FIRST HALF of the Third Act will be all about the protagonist's reacting to the Third Plot Point. He will have to gather his remaining resources and figure out what to do next. Even though the protagonist possesses the ultimate weapon of the Truth, the Third Plot Point has left him at a serious disadvantage. He will have only one chance left to hit the antagonistic force—and it's a long shot at best.

Since this segment will be a comparatively quiet and thoughtful sequel to the Third Plot Point, it provides a good opportunity to have the protagonist outright discuss the Truth and the Lie, and why he has chosen (and re-chosen) to be so committed to it.

(For more information about the First Half of the Third Act in a Flat Arc, see Chapter 17 in *Creating Character Arcs*.)

How can you up the stakes after the Third Plot Point by compounding your character's misery? _____

_____

_____ .

How can you give the character a reason to at least momentarily be rueful about his

decision to embrace the Truth (e.g., he feels maybe he did the *right* thing, but not the

smart thing)? _____

_____

_____ .

How will your character gain mastery over his pain and rise again with an even more solid conviction, believing the Truth is worth the price? _____

_____

_____

_____.

EXAMPLE:

- Even after learning his best friend is the enemy's Winter Soldier, Steve moves forward in faithfulness to his new allies and in a firm devotion to his Truth—even though he knows it may cost them their lives. (*Captain America: The Winter Soldier*)

How can your supporting characters demonstrate the positive impact the protagonist's Truth has had upon their lives? _____

_____

_____

_____.

How can these characters (who previously *needed* support), now offer support to your protagonist? _____

_____

_____.

EXAMPLE:

- Juba and the other gladiators rally around Maximus, in support of his plot to dethrone Commodus and reinstate the Republic. (*Gladiator*)

How is the world different in the Third Act from what it was in the First Act? _____

_____

_____

_____

_____.

How can you demonstrate this by giving one of your supporting characters the opportunity to support your protagonist by symbolically rejecting the temptation of the Lie in a physical way? _____

_____

_____

_____.

EXAMPLE:

- As Marianne grows more thoughtful and sensible, she also grows more aware of and caring toward Elinor's own disappointed hopes. (*Sense & Sensibility*)

THE CLIMAX

WHERE DOES IT BELONG?

From the 88% mark to the 98% mark in your story.

THE CLIMAX BEGINS roughly halfway through the Third Act. This is where your protagonist puts into play his final assault against the antagonistic force. Just as in a Positive Change Arc, the protagonist's Truth will be directly pitted against the antagonistic force's Lie. These two intangibles will be far more important in deciding the battle than will any display of physical power.

The difference between the Climax in a Positive Change Arc and the Climax in a Flat Arc is that the Flat-Arc protagonist is already completely solid in his own belief of the Truth. The antagonistic force will fling the Lie in the character's face and try to get him to weaken, but the protagonist won't budge. Even if the antagonist gets the upper hand physically, he will discover his own ineffectiveness in the face of the protagonist's resolve.

Supporting characters who are following Change Arcs may reach a climactic moment when their devotion to the Truth is tested one last time, but the prominence you give these moments will depend on the characters' importance to the story. The protagonist always needs to be the primary catalyst in the final victory.

(For more information about the Climax in a Flat Arc, see Chapter 17 in *Creating Character Arcs*.)

What form will the final confrontation between the protagonist and the antagonistic

force take? _____

_____.

EXAMPLES:

- Naval battle.
  (*Master and Commander*)

- Horse race.
  (*The Reivers*)

- Filibuster.
  (*Mr. Smith Goes to Washington*)

Where will your Climax take place? _____.

How does this setting symbolically emphasize the central conflict and the

theme? _____.

How does this setting physically or emotionally make the confrontation with

the antagonist more difficult? _____

_____.

How is the nature of the final climactic confrontation perfectly suited to force the protagon-

ist to use her Truth to its utmost against the antagonistic force? _____

_____

_____.

How will the antagonistic force attempt to use the Lie against the protagonist

one last time—and fail? _____

_____

_____.

How will the protagonist use her Truth to overcome the antagonistic force

and remove the last obstacle between herself and her main plot goal? _____

_____

_____

_____.

Will the protagonist's Truth change the antagonistic force in a deeper way than just making him impotent to bar her from her plot goal? How? _____

_____

_____

_____.

What one moment have readers been waiting for since the beginning of the story? ___

_____.

EXAMPLES:

- The kiss between the romantic leads.
  (*North & South*)

- The White Witch's death.
  (*The Lion, the Witch, and the Wardrobe*)

- The return of the hero's memory.
  (*Random Harvest*)

How can you deliver this moment? _____

_____.

How can supporting characters who have been changed by the Lie reach a minor climactic moment of their own, in which their devotion to their new Truth is tested? _____

_____

_____

_____

_____.

THE RESOLUTION
WHERE DOES IT BELONG?

From the 98% mark to the 100% mark in your story.

AS IN ANY type of story, the Resolution exists to prove how the conflict has changed either the characters or the world. In a Flat Arc, the changes will be most evident in the supporting cast and the world around the protagonist. The Truth will now be ascendant over the Lie. Supporting characters who were changed by the Truth will need to be presented in closing characteristic moments that prove the new direction their lives are now about to take. Supporting characters who believed the Truth all along will now be free to embrace and practice it.

(For more information about the Resolution in a Flat Arc, see Chapter 17 in *Creating Character Arcs*.)

Now that the main conflict has been resolved, what is your character planning to do next? _____

_____

_____

_____

_____

_____

_____

_____

_____.

Which of the following best describes the setting of your Resolution?

- ☐ The protagonist returns to the same Truth-filled Normal World from the First Act, able once again to live there in peace.

EXAMPLE:

- Mattie returns from her adventure in the Indian Nation, where she brought her father's murderer to justice and lost her arm, to the Normal World of her family's peaceful home in Yell County, Arkansas. (*True Grit*)

- ☐ The protagonist has escaped the Lie-ridden world into a new Truth-filled world, where she can make a new life.

EXAMPLE:

- Ginger and the others escape the chicken farm to make a new home for themselves where they can feel the grass beneath their feet. (*Chicken Run*)

- ☐ The protagonist has transformed the Lie-ridden Adventure World into a new Truth-filled Normal World, where he will make a new life.

EXAMPLE:

- Elinor and her family have learned to thrive in the stark Devonshire country where they first felt such outsiders.

- ☐ The protagonist has transformed the Lie-ridden Adventure World into a new Truth-filled Normal World, which he will journey away from.

EXAMPLE:

- Maximus restores Marcus Aurelius's dream of a Roman republic, but at the cost of his own life. (*Gladiator*)

Name three ways you can contrast the Normal World from the beginning of the story with the new and better normal.

1. _____.

2. _____.

3. _____.

Name four minor characters who have experienced new growth into the Truth thanks to the protagonist's actions in the conflict:

Character   **How Changed**

1._____   1._____

2._____   2._____

3._____   3._____

4._____   4._____

How will your Resolution answer the Thematic Question you asked in the first chapter? _____

_____

_____.

How can you visually *show* the character's new thematic Truth without slapping

readers in the face with the "moral of the story"? _____

_____

_____

_____.

How will your final scene be an upbeat one that demonstrates the hope of a new and

better day dawning for the protagonist's world? _____

_____

_____

_____.

CREATIVE EXERCISE:

In one sentence, describe the Truth Your Character Believes. In another sentence, expand it into your story's Thematic Question. This is the question the story is asking about the protagonist in particular and the world in general. It can be something as grand in scale as, "Do humans have the right to make war upon one another?" or as intimate as, "Can a parent be blamed for a child's mistakes?"

SOMETHING TO THINK ABOUT:

1. When will your protagonist first become aware of the threat of the Lie?
2. Is the character's main plot goal directly related to defeating the Lie in the world around him? If not, why will he have to overcome the Lie in order to reach his main plot goal?
3. Throughout the First Act, how can you use the Lie to prove what is at stake for the protagonist?
4. How will the protagonist's enemies end by becoming even more entrenched in the Lie?

RESOURCES:

- "The Impact Character: Why Every Character Arc Needs One," helpingwritersbecomeauthors.com/impact-character-2
- "5 Secrets of Complex Supporting Characters," helpingwritersbecomeauthors.com/complex-supporting-characters
- "Is This the Single Best Way to Write Powerful Themes?," helpingwritersbecomeauthors.com/single-best-way-write-powerful-themes
- "How to Choose the Right Antagonist for Your Story," helpingwritersbecomeauthors.com/how-to-choose-the-right-antagonist
- "6 Types of Courageous Characters," helpingwritersbecomeauthors.com/6-types-of-courageous-characters

3

THE NEGATIVE CHANGE ARC #1: DISILLUSIONMENT

CHARACTER BELIEVES LIE > OVERCOMES LIE >
NEW TRUTH IS TRAGIC

EVERYBODY LIKES A happy ending, but, let's face it, not all stories *have* happy endings. Negative Change Arcs have the ability to create stories of unparalleled power and resonance—*if they're true*. Truth resonates whether it's happy or hard, and some of the hardest truths to swallow are the most important for any of us to understand.

That's where your ability to wield Negative Change Arcs will come in handy. Negative Change Arcs tell the story of characters who end in worse places than those in which they started—and probably drag others down with them as well.

There are far more ways to do things wrong than there are ways to do things right, and so it goes with character arcs. While the Positive Change Arc and the Flat Arc both have one basic manifestation, the Negative Change Arc can follow several variations.

The first one we're going to look at is the Disillusionment Arc. In many ways, the Disillusionment Arc isn't negative at all. Just as in a Positive Change Arc, the protagonist is growing into a better understanding of the Truth. Possibly the character's life will even be changed for the better. And yet the story is still a downer. The character is moving from a positive outlook to a negative one. His new Truth isn't health and happiness; it's cold hard facts.

NEGATIVE CHANGE ARC #1: DISILLUSIONMENT

CHARACTER BELIEVES LIE >
OVERCOMES LIE >
NEW TRUTH IS TRAGIC

THIRD ACT

Resolution - Disillusioned with new Truth

Climactic Moment - Fully acknowledges Truth

Climax - Wields dark new Truth in final confrontation

3rd PLOT POINT - Accepts that comforting Lie is now completely nonexistent

SECOND ACT

2nd Pinch Point - Growing frustration with old Lie and disillusionment with new Truth

MIDPOINT (2nd PLOT POINT) - Moment of Truth : Forced to face Truth, but unwilling to embrace it

1st Pinch Point - Punished for using Lie

FIRST ACT

1st PLOT POINT - Full immersion in Adventure World's stark Truth

Inciting Event - First hint Lie is untrue

Hook - Believes Lie in comfortable Normal World

100%
98%
88%
75%
62%
50%
37%
25%
12%
1%

HelpingWritersBecomeAuthors.com

THE LIE YOUR CHARACTER BELIEVES

JUST AS IN a Positive Change Arc, the Disillusionment-Arc character will begin the story ignorant that he is living a Lie. Unlike the Positive-Arc character, however, the Disillusionment-Arc protagonist's Lie is one that seems to contribute to his health and happiness. He might believe the world is nothing but sunshine and roses, because his naivety and inexperience have yet to show him the darker side of the world.

The character's Lie, although seemingly perhaps even a positive thing at the beginning of the story, will render him ill-equipped to deal with the real world when he first encounters these strange, but undeniable new Truths.

(For more about the Lie Your Character Believes, see Chapters 1 and 18 in *Creating Character Arcs*.)

Write down four possible variations of the Lie Your Character Believes. Each one should be a specific belief, stated in one short sentence.

EXAMPLE:

- Nick Carraway explains his optimistic Lie right from the start: people—especially rich, beautiful, popular ones—are exactly who they seem, and the lives of the East Egg residents must, therefore, be reaching the pinnacle of happiness.
  (*The Great Gatsby*)

- Rookie cop Jake Hoyt's Lie is simplistic and idealistic view of what it means to be a police officer: cops are good guys who catch the bad guys.
  (*Training Day*)

Lie #1: _____

_____.

Lie #2: _____

_____.

Lie #3: _____

_____.

Lie #4: _____

_____.

How can each of these potential Lies be reflected in your character's exterior world and/or how can the exterior world be a metaphor for your character's inner struggle?

EXAMPLES:

• Nick views the sparkling world of his cousin Daisy's upscale New York society life as something that must be worthwhile due to its beauty and ease.

Exterior World Reflection for Lie #1: _____

_____.

Exterior World Reflection for Lie #2: _____

_____.

Exterior World Reflection for Lie #3: _____

_____.

Exterior World Reflection for Lie #4: _____

_____.

Which of these four Lies will be the primary Lie for your character's arc? Which one best influences your plot and theme?

☐ Lie #1
☐ Lie #2
☐ Lie #3
☐ Lie #4

Final Choice of the Lie Your Character Believes: _____

_____

_____

_____

_____.

THE THING YOUR CHARACTER NEEDS

HOWEVER DARK AND discouraging the Truth in a Disillusionment Arc, it is still the Thing Your Character Needs. It is still true, and it has the ability to set the character free—if only he could learn to stop mourning the beautiful Lie. Disillusionment-Arc characters will almost always be better off and better able to survive without their Lies. However, they find the cold, hard Truth of little solace in the aftermath of the difficult lessons they learn on the way to discovering it.

(For more information about the Thing Your Character Needs, see Chapters 2 and 18 in *Creating Character Arcs*.)

What Truth opposes the Lie Your Character Believes? _____

_____

_____

_____

_____

_____

_____

_____.

EXAMPLE:

- Corruption is often gilded.
  (*The Great Gatsby*)

- Morality on the streets is full of shades of gray.
  (*Training Day*)

Write down four possible ways your story's Truth can manifest as a specific Thing Your Character Needs. This will be a specific action or belief on your character's part.

EXAMPLE:

- Reject the hypocritical lifestyle of the immoral elite.
- Fight back against corruption by first realizing its complexities.

Thing Your Character Needs #1: _____

_____.

Thing Your Character Needs #2: _____

_____

_____.

Thing Your Character Needs #3: _____

_____

_____.

Thing Your Character Needs #4: _____

_____

_____.

How might your character *act* upon each of these four options at the end of the story, to demonstrate she has gained an understanding and acceptance of the Truth?

EXAMPLE:

- Nick leaves the city and cuts ties with his rich cousin and her husband.
- Jake muddies his own previously squeaky-clean reputation to retrieve stolen money from Alonzo and leave him to be killed by Russian mosters.

Action based on Thing Your Character Needs #1: _____

_____.

Action based on Thing Your Character Needs #2: _____

_____.

Action based on Thing Your Character Needs #3: _____

_____.

Action based on Thing Your Character Needs #4: _____

_____.

Which of these four options will be the primary Thing Your Character Needs in this story? Which one best reflects your story's Truth?

☐ Thing Your Character Needs #1
☐ Thing Your Character Needs #2
☐ Thing Your Character Needs #3
☐ Thing Your Character Needs #4

Final Choice of the Thing Your Character Needs: _____

_____

_____

_____.

How do you see the Truth manifesting externally/visually at the end of your story? _

_____

_____.

THE THING YOUR CHARACTER WANTS

THE THING YOUR Character Wants is what drives his main story goal. Based upon the false perceptions of his Lie, he desires something that, on its surface, seems a worthy goal. However, because his understanding of what his desire truly encompasses is incomplete, he fails to realize he is chasing after more than he is bargaining for. This goal will drive him throughout the story, but as the plot progresses and his eyes are opened more and more to the Truth, he will begin to realize the Thing He Wants either isn't so desirable after all or simply isn't worth the price.

(For more information about the Thing Your Character Wants, see Chapters 2 and 18 in *Creating Character Arcs*.)

Write down four possible Things Your Character Wants. These are deep primal desires. They are *not* necessarily your character's story goal, but they will influence the specific goal.

EXAMPLES:

- Fit into society.
  (*The Great Gatsby*)

- Become a detective.
  (*Training Day*)

Desire #1: _____

_____

_____.

Desire #2: _____

_____

_____.

Desire #3: _____

_____.

Desire #4: _____

_____.

What specific story goal arises from each of these desires? This will be the plot goal your character will be working toward over the course of your entire story.

EXAMPLES:

- Meet and cultivate the friendship of the wealthy and fabulous Jay Gatsby.
- Successfully get through his training day with crooked cop Alonzo.

Goal Arising From Desire #1: _____

_____

_____.

Goal Arising From Desire #2: _____

_____

_____.

Goal Arising From Desire #3: _____

_____

_____.

Goal Arising From Desire #4: _____

_____.

Which of these four desires will be the primary Thing Your Character Wants in this story? Which one best guides your plot and theme?

☐ Desire #1
☐ Desire #2
☐ Desire #3
☐ Desire #4

Final Choice of the Thing Your Character Wants: _____

_____

_____.

Which of the four goals will be your character's primary plot goal in this story? Which one best represents the Thing He Wants and drives your plot?

☐ Goal #1
☐ Goal #2
☐ Goal #3
☐ Goal #4

Final Choice of Character's Plot Goal: _____

_____

_____

_____.

THE CHARACTERISTIC MOMENT

THE ACTUAL STRUCTURE of the character arc begins with the Characteristic Moment. The Characteristic Moment aligns with the structural Hook, which shows up the moment your protagonist does—presumably in the first chapter.

The Characteristic Moment is your protagonist's big debut. He steps onto the stage, the spotlight hits him—and he shines. In this one moment, he shows readers what he's all about: the good, the bad, and the potential for disillusionment to come. The Characteristic Moment shows readers exactly why this protagonist is going to be worth reading about.

(For more information about the Characteristic Moment, see Chapters 4 and 18 in *Creating Character Arcs*.)

EXAMPLE:

- A narrative introduction from Nick's older self, explaining why he visited New York in his youth.
  (*The Great Gatsby*)

- A view of a nervous and hopeful Jake, leaving the wife and child he obviously cherishes, to embark on his long-awaited "training day"—in the hopes both of fulfilling his own idealistic ideas of being a police officer and to provide his family with a better life. (*Training Day*)

Before you can craft the perfect Characteristic Moment, you must first know something about your character. Answer the following questions for starters (and for a full character interview, see my books *Outlining Your Novel* and the *Outlining Your Novel Workbook*).

What is this character's role in the story?

       ☐ Protagonist

       ☐ Antagonist

       ☐ Mentor

       ☐ Sidekick

       ☐ Love Interest

       ☐ Other: _____

What is your character's name? _____.

How old is your character? _____.

Of what nationality is your character? _____.

What is your character's occupation or primary identity (e.g., stay-at-home mom, rebel

soldier)? _____

_____.

Does the character have any important physical characteristics (e.g., a limp, green

scales)? _____

_____.

Name three prevailing aspects of the character's personality (e.g., kindness, quick
temper, wit):

     1. _____.

     2. _____.

     3. _____.

What *one* important personality trait, virtue, or skill best sums up your character? ____

_____.

     How can you dramatize this aspect of your character to its fullest extent? ____

     _____

     _____.

How can you dramatize this aspect in a way that also introduces the plot? ____

_____

_____.

What do you want readers to find most sympathetic and/or interesting about this charac-

ter? _____

_____.

How can you dramatize this aspect of your character in an opening scene? __

_____

_____.

What is your character's overall story goal and/or the Thing He Wants Most?_____

_____

_____.

How can you set up this goal or show the coming need for it in an opening

scene? _____

_____.

What is your character's scene goal in the opening chapter? _____

_____

_____.

How will you dramatize this scene goal right from the start of your opening

scene? _____

_____.

How will the character's pursuit of this goal meet with an obvious obstacle (i.e.,

conflict)? _____

_____.

How will this goal move the plot, either by immediately causing consequences or

setting them up for later? _____

_____

_____.

How can any of the above help you demonstrate, or at least hint at, your character's

Lie? _____

_____.

How can you craft the above elements to make your protagonist immediately appeal-

ing to readers (e.g., what's keeping them from looking away?)? _____

_____

_____

_____.

Which of your character's strengths can you show readers right away? _____

_____

_____

_____

_____.

Which of your character's pertinent weaknesses (especially Lie-driven weaknesses) can

you show readers right away? _____

_____

_____

_____

_____.

List events or activities you can use in your opening chapter to dramatize all the of above. Try to think of "big" moments that are unique, visually engaging, and keep the characters in motion.

1. _____.

2. _____.

3. _____.

4. _____.

5. _____.

Write a summary of your opening chapter and how you will introduce your character in a memorable and engaging Characteristic Moment: _____

_____

_____

_____

_____

_____

_____

_____

_____

_____

_____

_____

_____

_____

Which of the following does your proposed Characteristic Moment accomplish?

- ☐ Introduce character.
- ☐ Reveal character's name.
- ☐ Indicate character's gender.
- ☐ Indicate character's age group.
- ☐ Indicate character's nationality.
- ☐ Indicate character's occupation/main identity.
- ☐ Indicate any important physical characteristics.
- ☐ Indicate role in the story (i.e., protagonist).
- ☐ Demonstrate prevailing aspect of personality.
- ☐ Hook readers' sympathy and/or interest.
- ☐ Demonstrate scene goal.
- ☐ Indicate story goal.
- ☐ Demonstrate (or at least hint at) Lie.
- ☐ Move plot directly or through foreshadowing.

If you're unable to combine the majority of the above elements into one scene, answer whether it would work better to divide the necessary characteristic elements into two or more scenes.

_____

_____

_____

_____

_____

_____

THE NORMAL WORLD

THE CHARACTERISTIC MOMENT is only half of a good character arc's opening. It gives readers a character, but the character still needs context. The Normal World provides that context. At its most basic level, the Normal World is—as its name suggests—a setting. This is the place in which your story opens. It is a place in which your character has found contentment—or at least complacency.

The Normal World plays a vital role in grounding the First Act of your story in a concrete setting. Even more important, the Normal World creates the standard against which all the personal and plot changes to come will be measured. Without this vivid opening example of what will change in your character's life, the rest of the arc will lack definition and potency.

(For more information about the Normal World, see Chapters 5 and 18 in *Creating Character Arcs*.)

EXAMPLE:

- Nick's Normal World (which readers never see but are told about) is a small Midwestern town that has cultivated both his own sense of right and wrong, as well as his naivety about humanity's true potential for personal corruption.
  (*The Great Gatsby*)

- The exterior of Jake's Normal World is only briefly glimpsed, in the ordinary home life of a loving but hard-working family who is just scraping by. He carries his interior Normal World with him into his training day with Alonzo, via his mistaken expectations of what being an undercover narcotics detective is really like.
  (*Training Day*)

Briefly describe the physical setting of the Normal World (e.g., Chicago or Mars): ___

_____

_____

_____.

How does your chosen Normal World symbolically represent the Lie Your Character

Believes? _____

_____

_____

_____

_____.

EXAMPLE:

- Nick's wholesome but naïve Midwestern upbringing is ironically presented in his father's advice: "Just remember all the people in this world haven't had the advantages you've had."
- Jake's honest and earnest home life with his wife and daughter represent a safe world that has never been challenged by the hard facts of criminal corruption.

How will the Normal World visibly prove to readers (*show* them) your protagonist's

"before" state at the beginning of the story? _____

_____.

What setting for the Normal World provides the most logical backstory for *why* your

character believes the Lie? _____

_____.

What is holding your protagonist in the Normal World that has kept him from leaving it

before now? _____

_____.

How is your chosen Normal World empowering your character to continue believing

his Lie by giving him no reason to look beyond it? _____

_____

_____

_____.

How will the Normal World contrast with the Adventure World that will follow in

the next two acts? _____

_____.

Which of the following will best describe the Adventure World of your story's main conflict?

☐   A dramatically new and different setting.

EXAMPLE:

- Nick leaves his Midwestern hometown to experience life in New York City.

☐   The same physical setting as the Normal World, with only facets of the world changing.

EXAMPLE:

- Jake enters the Adventure World when he steps into senior detective Alonzo's car to begin his training day.

When your protagonist is later forced out of the Normal World into the Second Act,

how will this begin to shake his belief in the Lie? _____

_____

_____.

Will the character return to the Normal World at the end of the story?

☐ Yes

☐ No

If the Normal World remains a legitimately good place, how will the protagonist's

dark new perspective of the Truth put him at odds within it? _____

_____

_____.

If the Normal World remains a place limited by the Lie, how will the protagon-

ist have moved past his ability to fit in there? _____

_____

_____

_____.

If the protagonist impacted the Normal World over the course of the story,

how will it have grown disillusioned by the end as well? _____

_____

_____

_____

_____

_____.

THE FIRST ACT

WHERE DOES IT BELONG?

From the 1% mark to the 25% mark in your story.

JUST AS IN a Positive Change Arc, the Disillusionment Arc is about the protagonist overcoming the Lie She Believes. Here, however, her "ignorance is bliss." Her eyes are about to be opened to the cold, hard Truth of life, but in a way that disillusions her instead of empowering her. She starts out believing what seems to be a lovely, idealistic Lie, only to have the blinders ripped away.

(For more information about the First Act in a Disillusionment Arc, see Chapter 18 in *Creating Character Arcs*.)

How will you reinforce/dramatize the character's Lie? _____

_____

_____

_____.

How will you show how the character is content in his Lie, via a hopeful or even idealis-

tic view of the world? _____

_____

_____.

How will you demonstrate the Thing Your Character Wants and the Thing He Needs?

_____

_____

_____.

How will his Characteristic Moment illustrate or hint at the Lie? _____

_____

_____.

How will his Normal World immediately illustrate or hint at the Lie? _____

_____

_____.

Name three ways you will continue to reinforce the Lie or introduce more of its facets throughout the First Act:

    1. _____.

    2. _____.

    3. _____.

How can you hint at your character's latent incompatibility with the Truth? _____

_____

_____

_____.

EXAMPLE:

- Nick is a decent Midwestern young man, who is fundamentally incapable of compromising in order to live in harmony with the Truth about rich society: its corruption and selfishness.
  (*The Great Gatsby*)

- Early on in the training day, Jake is shocked and horrified by Alonzo's actions, especially when Alonzo brutally confiscates pot and then coerces Jake into smoking it.
  (*Training Day*)

What specific character quality will be intrinsic to dragging your character into an awareness of the Truth, even though he doesn't want to recognize it?_____

_____.

Even if this trait isn't yet fully developed, how can you hint right from the beginning that the seed is there? _____

_____

_____.

How can you begin giving the character small hints about the falsity of the Lie and the dark nature of the Truth? _____

_____

_____.

EXAMPLE:

- Even though Nick is dazzled by the extravagant displays of wealth he witnesses at his cousin Daisy's, and then at the opulent parties of the mysterious Gatsby, already the hints of gilded corruption are visible.

- Even though Alonzo's smooth words and arguments confuse Jake at first, Alonzo's actions reveal his corruption almost from the start, as he does things to deliberately shock and rattle Jake's complacent view of "incorruptible" police officers.

What Inciting Event will be the Call to Adventure that first brushes your character against the main conflict? _____

_____.

- After arriving in New York, Nick visits his cousin Daisy in East Egg and learns both about his lavish and mysterious neighbor Jay Gatsby and the affair Daisy's husband Tom is having with another woman.

- Rookie cop Jake, on his training day with veteran cop Alonzo, gets his first indication of the Truth of Alonzo's corruption when Alonzo demands he smoke confiscated pot.

How will this Inciting Event set up the character's entry into the Adventure World of the

main conflict in the Second Act? _____

_____

_____.

Does the Inciting Event initially seem:

☐ a good thing.

☐ a bad thing.

How will the Call to Adventure initially be met with resistance or refusal? _____

_____

_____.

EXAMPLE:

- Even as Nick eagerly engages with Daisy's "sophisticated" city life, he almost immediately feels stirrings of discomfort and resistance to the decadence and cynicism she and others in her set display. He sees Gatsby for the first time, but decides not to wave to him.

- Jake is initially incredulous and resistant to Alonzo's demand, in part because he knows he could get kicked off the force for it.

Will the protagonist be the one to initially reject the Call to Adventure, or will some

one else try to reject it for him? _____.

How long will it take the protagonist to stop resisting?

    ☐ Entire rest of the First Act up to the First Plot Point.

    ☐ Shorter period ending with what event_____.

How does the Inciting Event change the protagonist's awareness of and comfort in

the Normal World in however small or subconscious a way? _____

_____

_____

_____.

How will your protagonist still be entrenched in the Lie toward the end of the First

Act? _____

_____

_____.

How will his subconscious attitude toward the negativity of the Truth take its first

step forward? _____

_____

_____

_____

_____

_____.

- Throughout the First Act, Nick still holds a rosy view of high society, but the first bits of tarnish show through when his cousin Daisy's brutish husband Tom drags him to a tawdry party with his mistress Myrtle.

- Even as Jake resists Alonzo's somewhat amused, somewhat cruel insistence that his views are simplistic and idealistic, he obviously can't help seeing the truth of Alonzo's words. The seeds of discomfort are planted, and his cognitive dissonance begins to grow.

What will the protagonist decide to *do* about the Call to Adventure at the Inciting

Event? _____

_____

_____

_____.

EXAMPLE:

- A bit reluctantly, Nick agrees to let Tom show him around town, only to realize the trip was a screen to allow Tom to visit his mistress.

- Jake succumbs to Alonzo's insistence and smokes the pot, both giving himself a glimpse into Alonzo's shadow world and unwittingly putting himself under Alonzo's thumb by providing blackmail material.

THE FIRST PLOT POINT

WHERE DOES IT BELONG?

25% of the way into your story.

N O MATTER HOW comparatively positive the First Plot Point may seem, it must always be dogged by the portent of bad things to come. Foreshadowing must be wielded deftly in Negative Change Arcs more than in any other. In order for an unhappy ending to resonate with readers, they must be prepared for it. They must feel it was the only logical outcome.

(For more information about the First Plot Point in a Disillusionment Arc, see Chapter 19 in *Creating Character Arcs*.)

What event occurs at the end of the First Act that causes your character to leave the

Normal World and irreversibly engage with the main conflict?_____

_____

_____.

EXAMPLE:

- At one of Gatsby's extraordinary parties, Nick finally meets the man himself when Gatsby takes him under his wing.
  (*The Great Gatsby*)

- After Alonzo takes Jake to Roger, a former narcotics officer turned drug dealer, Jake notices two thugs trying to rape a girl in an alley. He intervenes, despite Alonzo's disapproval. Alonzo lets the thugs go free and sends the girl home.
  (*Training Day*)

In what way might this event be surprising even after the Inciting Event?_____

_____

_____.

Which of the following best describes your First Plot Point?

☐ A seemingly positive opportunity.

☐ Something disastrous.

What decision on your character's part led him right up to the First Plot Point, making him at least partially responsible for what happens? (See also the final question in the last section.) _____

_____.

EXAMPLE:

- Nick greatly desires an introduction to Gatsby, who seems to symbolize everything he believes about the glittering social realm.

- Jake goes along with everything Alonzo tells him to do, despite his growing reluctance and disbelief.

Which of the following best describes your First Plot Point?

☐ It physically removes the protagonist from the Normal World.

EXAMPLE:

- Nick steps from his own humble existence into the rarefied air of Gatsby's circle.

☐ It warps the Normal World, forcing the protagonist to adapt to new ways of surviving within it.

EXAMPLE:

- Jake is shifted from the safety of his squeaky-clean rookie days to the confusing, dangerous, and morally ambiguous world of a street detective.

Which best describes your protagonist's reaction to the First Plot Point?

☐ Enthusiasm—she wants to enter the conflict of the Second Act.

☐ Resistance—she has to be forced to enter the conflict of the Second Act.

After the First Plot Point, how will your protagonist react? _____

_____

_____

_____.

What definitive action will he take to move forward into the Adventure World

of the main conflict? _____

_____.

Name three new physical needs that must be met in the aftermath of the First Plot
Point:

1. _____.

2. _____.

3. _____.

What definitive new plot goal will the character now adopt (something quantifiable,

based on the Thing He Wants)? _____

_____

_____.

Do you want the character to ultimately achieve this goal?

☐ Yes.
   Why? _____.

☐ No.
   Why? _____.

How will the character's decisions and actions in the aftermath of the First Plot Point

drag her out of complacency and force her onto a path toward eventually facing the

Truth?_____

_____

_____

_____.

What about the Adventure World of the Second Act makes the character's Lie less

believable than it was in the Normal World? _____

_____

_____

_____

_____

_____

_____.

THE FIRST HALF OF THE SECOND ACT

WHERE DOES IT BELONG?

From the 25% mark to the 50% mark in your story.

AS ALWAYS, THE First Half of the Second Act is all about the character's reaction to the First Plot Point. He's also learning more about the Lie and the Truth. In a Disillusionment Arc, he's encountering difficulties in pursuing the Lie, even as he's getting closer to the Thing He Wants while simultaneously getting farther away from the Thing He Needs.

(For more information about the First Half of the Second Act in a Disillusionment Arc, see Chapter 19 in *Creating Character Arcs*.)

What catalyst (possibly in the form of information from another character) will your

character begin to receive that pushes him to see the cracks in his Lie? _____

_____

_____

_____

_____.

EXAMPLE:

- Gatsby introduces Nick to his underworld associate Meyer Wolf sheim, which prompts Nick to realize Gatsby's fortune has been illegally obtained through bootlegging.
  (*The Great Gatsby*)

- Recognizing Jake is upset that he released the rape "suspects," Alonzo smoothly explains why Jake should remain a patrol cop of he wants to "run and gun," but that if he wants to be an investigative officer he must overlook smaller crimes into order to go after the big fish.
  (*Training Day*)

How can other characters *show* your protagonist the Truth, rather than just *telling* her

about it? _____

_____

_____

_____

_____.

How is your protagonist feeling slightly out of place within the new Adventure World

of the Second Act? _____

_____

_____.

What old Lie-based belief is the protagonist still using to try to reach his goals? _____

_____.

How are these old Lie-based actions proving less useful in the Second Act than they

did in the First? _____

_____.

EXAMPLE:
- Nick wants to balance his belief in the beauty of Daisy's world with his own Midwestern ethics, but he finds it increasingly impossible in the swirl of Gatsby's glitter.
- Jake repeatedly tries to reinforce his own views of a cop's moral code, only to have Alonzo convincingly explain why that code doesn't hold up in the real world.

How is the protagonist demonstrating confusion or frustration about why his old methods are no longer working for him? _____

_____

_____.

What first move will he make to slowly begin evolving his tactics to avoid his Lie-based failures so far? _____

_____

_____.

How is the character pursuing the Thing She Wants in the Second Act? _____

_____

_____.

How is she getting closer to achieving her plot goal? _____

_____

_____.

How is her pursuit of the Thing She Wants pushing her away from the Thing She Needs? _____

_____

_____

_____.

If the character continues down this path unchecked, what personal, spiritual, and perhaps even physical destruction would she end up running into? _____

_____

_____

_____.

EXAMPLE:

- Nick's future, should he follow the path of Gatsby and others, is clearly reflected in the lives of everyone around him in East and West Egg.
- Alonzo is clearly an image of what Jake will become if he continues down the path to Alonzo's Truth.

THE MIDPOINT

WHERE DOES IT BELONG?

50% of the way into your story.

THROUGHOUT THE FIRST Half of the Second Act, the protagonist has been slowly realizing the Truth is different from what he has so far believed it to be. He hasn't completely accepted this new Truth *as* true, but he has been struggling with the cognitive dissonance caused by the fact that reality isn't matching up with his preexisting idealistic view.

Now, at the Midpoint, he will receive a resounding revelation—a Moment of Truth—that will bring him face to face with that Truth. He will still cling to his Lie, wanting to somehow fit it together with the Truth, to make it still *work*. But from the Midpoint on, his eyes have been opened to the dark Truth and he will be increasingly unable to escape it.

(For more information about the Midpoint in a Disillusionment Arc, see Chapter 19 in *Creating Character Arcs*.)

What is your story's Midpoint event? _____

_____

_____

_____.

EXAMPLE:

- Nick realizes Gatsby has lied about his dramatic past and his rise to wealth.
  (*The Great Gatsby*)

- Alonzo takes Jake to a meeting with the "Three Wise Men," high-ranking and equally corrupt officials, who trade Alonzo an arrest warrant for illegally obtained cash, so Alonzo can try to get clear with the angry Russian Mafia. Jake realizes for the first time how deep the corruption goes.
  (*Training Day*)

What can you do to make this centerpiece scene as "big" as possible? _____

_____

_____

_____.

How have the events of the First Half of the Second Act led up to the Midpoint by

slowly forcing your protagonist to recognize the uselessness of some of the Lie-

based tactics he has tried to use to reach his goal? _____

_____

_____

_____.

How will the external events of the Midpoint prompt a "Moment of Truth," in which

the character sees the inevitability of the Truth? _____

_____

_____.

Example:

- Nick helps Gatsby arrange a manic romantic reunion with Daisy, during which Nick visits Gatsby's house and sees proof revealing Gatsby is a liar and a fake.

- After meeting the Three Wise Men, Jake realizes Alonzo isn't the single corrupt exception to his idealistic idea of a law officer. He can no longer escape the Truth of what Alonzo has been telling him all along—that to be a narcotics officer, compromises must be made.

How will the character remain unwilling to completely reject the Lie itself? _____

_____

_____

_____.

EXAMPLE:

- After the Midpoint, Nick becomes more and more disgusted with the lives of his rich friends, but he can't bring himself to abandon Gatsby and his impossibly optimistic insistence that he can somehow repeat his romantic past with the fickle Daisy.

- After learning about Alonzo trading the illegally-obtained $40,000 for an arrest warrant, a shocked Jake insists, "I didn't want to know." This sums up his entire mindset of resistance to the Truth up to this point: he would have chosen to remain in ignorance of how the world of undercover cops really worked.

    During the rest of the Second Act, how will you demonstrate your character's

    deepening inner conflict—caught between comfortable Lie and unavoidable

    Truth? _____

    _____

    _____.

How will this Midpoint realization help the character better understand the true na-

ture of the conflict? _____

_____

_____

_____.

How will the events of the Midpoint act as a swivel between the two halves of your story—shifting your character out of uninformed reaction and into educated action?

_____

_____

_____.

How will the character's continuing inner conflict and resistance to the Truth continue to hold him back during the Second Act? _____

_____

_____

_____

_____.

THE SECOND HALF OF THE SECOND ACT

WHERE DOES IT BELONG?

From the 50% mark to the 75% mark in your story.

THE SECOND HALF of the Second Act in the Disillusionment Arc is where the character finally begins growing *into* the Truth, just as he would in a Positive Change Arc. Unlike the Positive Change Arc, however, the Truth here is one of destructive negativity that threatens to drag the protagonist down into darkness.

(For more information about the Second Half of the Second Act in a Disillusionment Arc, see Chapter 19 in *Creating Character Arcs*.)

How is the character acting on the Truth she discovered at the Midpoint? _____

_____

_____

_____

_____.

What new "tools" did the Moment of Truth provide your character that are allowing

him to make better progress toward the Thing He Wants? _____

_____

_____

_____

_____.

EXAMPLE:

- Thanks to the assistance he provided Gatsby at the Midpoint, Nick has now become his fast friend, and the gates of society open up to him as never before.
  (*The Great Gatsby*)

- Against his own moral code, Jake begins to go along with Alonzo's corrupt methods, beginning to believe Alonzo is right and that this type of violent compromise is the only way to succeed as a cop.
  (*Training Day*)

How is the Lie still present in the character's life, if only on a subconscious level? __

_____

_____

_____.

How is the character suffering cognitive dissonance as the result of clinging

to two incompatible beliefs? _____

_____

_____

_____.

How is his refusal to completely face the Truth preventing him from fully relin-

quishing his Lie? _____

_____

_____

_____.

What mistakes is the protagonist making within the external conflict as a result

of the Lie's continuing presence and his resultant inner conflict? _____

_____

_____

_____.

- Nick is no longer sure what he wants in the external plot. He plods along in his city life, but his heart is no longer so invested in the goal of fitting in with society.
- Still wanting to believe somehow that Alonzo is doing righteous work, Jake goes along when they kill the former cop-turned-dealer Roger for "resisting arrest," in order to get their hands on his money.

How is the character beginning to be drawn more and more to the Thing He Needs—and

paying for it by having to move farther away from the Thing He Wants? _____

_____

_____

_____

_____

_____.

- Nick begins to resist Gatsby and Daisy's romance, insisting Gatsby can't relive the past.
- Jake begins to grow resistant to Alonzo's bullying, hinting at the growing risk to both his promotion and his life.

Write down four scenes from the first half of the story in which your character demonstrated Lie-driven motives. Then brainstorm four scenes you can include in the second half that will contrast the earlier scenes by showing how your character's new understanding of the Truth has already started to change her.

"Before" Scenes

1._____

2._____

3._____

4._____

"After" Scenes

1._____

2._____

3._____

4._____

EXAMPLE:

- **Before:** Nick came to New York as a bright-eyed young man, eager to make friends and embrace an exciting new world.

- **After:** As his disillusionment with his rich friends grows, he offers a bleak observation on his thirtieth birthday: "Before me stretched the portentous menacing road of a new decade."

At the end of the Second Act, how will the Thing the Character Wants place itself

within the character's grasp, offering a seeming victory? _____

_____

_____.

Why is it necessary for the character to subject himself to the Lie if he is to claim the

Thing He Wants right now? _____

_____

_____

_____.

How can you dramatize the character's inner conflict in this section? _____

_____

_____

_____

_____.

Before the Second Act ends, how can you blatantly demonstrate the crux of your

character's arc? _____

_____

_____

_____

_____.

THE THIRD PLOT POINT

WHERE DOES IT BELONG?

75% of the way into your story.

NO MATTER WHAT type of arc you're writing, the Third Plot Point is always a place that reeks of death. The character is brought face to face with his mortality—either because his own life is threatened (literally or by extension, as when, for example, his livelihood or good name is under siege) or because the lives of those he cares about are put under the axe.

(For more information about the Third Plot Point in a Disillusionment Arc, see Chapter 20 in *Creating Character Arcs*.)

What Third Plot Point crisis will force your protagonist to a low moment in both the

inner and outer conflicts? _____

_____

_____.

EXAMPLE:

- After Daisy wavers in her decision to run away with Gatsby, a tremendous car accident occurs. Nick learns Gatsby's yellow roadster hit and killed Tom's mistress Myrtle.
  (*The Great Gatsby*)

- Alonzo leaves Jake at the house of a Mexican gang, whom he pays to kill Jake, while he goes to pay off the Russian Mafia.
  (*Training Day*)

What does the antagonistic force do to enact the reversal that occurs at the Third

Plot Point? _____

_____

_____.

How will your protagonist's main plot goal be dramatically (perhaps irrevocably) endangered as a result? _____

_____

_____.

How does the Third Plot Point finally cause the character to make a choice between the Thing She Wants and the Thing She Needs by forcing her to sacrifice one or the other? _____

_____

_____.

How can you make the consequences of this as painful as possible? _____

_____

_____

_____.

How can you make it as easy and empowering as possible for the character to choose the Lie and the Thing She Wants—making it all the harder for her to reject it? _____

_____

_____

_____.

What will finally prompt the character to fully recognize the dark Truth and

accept it even at the risk of the Thing She Wants? _____

_____

_____.

What irretrievable action will your character take in burning her bridges and

proving her grim acceptance of the Truth? _____

_____

_____.

How can you cast the pall of death over the Third Plot Point by featuring it either

literally or symbolically? _____

_____

_____

_____

_____

_____

_____.

THE FIRST HALF OF THE THIRD ACT

WHERE DOES IT BELONG?

From the 75% mark to the 88% mark in your story.

I N THIS SECTION between the Third Plot Point and the beginning of the Climax, the character will find himself in his darkest pit of disillusionment yet. He has just seen the true power of the Truth, and he can no longer escape that it *is* true. His comforting little Lie from the First Act is now just fluff, completely impotent to counter this fearsome reality.

It is at this point that the character will be faced with his final and most important dilemma: must he surrender to the darkness of this Truth, or will he be able to maintain his personal integrity and empowerment even in the face of the Truth—and even, sometimes, at the risk of his lifestyle or life?

(For more information about the First Half of the Third Act in a Disillusionment Arc, see Chapter 20 in *Creating Character Arcs*.)

How can you up the stakes after the Third Plot Point by compounding your character's

misery? _____

_____

_____

_____

_____

_____

_____.

Will the character have reason to at least momentarily regret his decision to acknowledge

the Truth (e.g., he feels maybe he did the *smart* thing, but not the *right* thing)? _____

_____.

How will your character gain mastery over his pain and rise with a new goal of how to

approach life as he now views it? _____

_____

_____

_____

_____.

EXAMPLE:

- Nick is utterly disillusioned with Daisy and Tom and their hypocritical selfishness. After the accident, he refuses to enter their home. He accepts the Truth, but he refuses to be party to it any longer. (*The Great Gatsby*)

- After escaping death at the hands of the Mexican gang members (who turn out to be related to the girl he saved in the First Plot Point), Jake realizes the police officials will do nothing to stop Alonzo and that if he's to do it himself, he must be willing, like Alonzo has told him all along, to do it outside the law. (*Training Day*)

Even after your character fully accepts the Truth, how can you keep him off-balance

by nudging him with reflexive longings for the Lie to be true? _____

_____

_____.

How will these futile longings in this section keep your character from being either completely fulfilled or completely effective in reorienting himself? _____

_____

_____

_____.

EXAMPLE:

- After learning Daisy is letting Gatsby take the rap for killing Myrtle, Nick stays in town to try to help Gatsby, but from that point on, he's no longer bewitched by the spectacles of wealth and beauty around him.

How is your character different in the Third Act from who he was in the First Act? _

_____

_____

_____.

How can you demonstrate this by giving your protagonist the opportunity to symbolically reject the Lie in a physical way? _____

_____

_____

_____.

EXAMPLE:

- Nick refuses to follow his big-city girlfriend Jordan into Tom and Daisy's house—a physical symbolism of his inner rejection of their lifestyle.
- Jake takes his gun in hand and hunts Alonzo down.

Prior to the Climax, how can you use a minor character (*other* than the main antagonist) to try to tempt the protagonist back into letting himself believe the Lie is still valid? _

_____

_____

_____.

Which of the following characters will you use for this renewed attack?

☐ Minor antagonist, named: _____.

☐ Skeptical or fearful ally, named: _____.

☐ Protagonist's inner doubts.

☐ Other: _____.

How will this attack specifically target the protagonist's own agony about his new Truth? _____

_____

_____

_____.

How will the Lie be presented in the most attractive terms possible? _____

_____

_____

_____.

How will the protagonist overcome his temptation and insist upon his new

Truth even more strongly? _____

_____

_____

_____

_____.

THE CLIMAX

WHERE DOES IT BELONG?

From the 88% mark to the 98% mark in your story.

IN PLANNING THE Climax in a Disillusionment Arc, look back at the person your character was in the beginning of the book. The Lie he embraced in the beginning—and the way he embraced it—should point you to an obvious culmination in the Climax.

(For more information about the Climax in a Disillusionment Arc, see Chapter 20 in *Creating Character Arcs*.)

How has your character recently proven *before* the Climax that she is a changed person? _____

_____.

What form will the final confrontation between the protagonist and the antagonistic force take? _____

_____

_____.

EXAMPLES:

- Naval battle.
  (*Master and Commander*)

- Horse race.
  (*The Reivers*)

- Filibuster.
  (*Mr. Smith Goes to Washington*)

Where will your Climax take place? _____

_____.

How does this setting symbolically emphasize the central conflict and the theme?_____.

How does this setting physically or emotionally make the confrontation with the antagonist more difficult? _____

_____.

How is the nature of the final climactic confrontation perfectly suited to provide the final test for your protagonist's new Truth, proving her total resignation to it? ____

_____

_____

_____.

How will the antagonist attempt to manipulate the protagonist one more time using her old Lie? _____

_____

_____

_____.

Which is most true of your story:

☐ The protagonist will sink into a defeated harmony with the new Truth.

☐ The protagonist will avoid the new Truth by walking away from its environs.

THE RESOLUTION

WHERE DOES IT BELONG?

From the 98% mark to the 100% mark in your story.

CREATE A CLOSING scene that drives home the character's final state. Death, insanity, war, destruction, imprisonment—whatever finds him in the end should be represented in the story's closing motif, as a clear contrast to how the story began.

(For more information about the Resolution in a Disillusionment Arc, see Chapter 20 in *Creating Character Arcs*.)

Now that the main conflict has been resolved, what is your character planning to do

next? _____

_____.

How will this choice for a new life contrast the choices the character would have

made back in the first chapter? _____

_____

_____.

EXAMPLE:

- In the beginning, Nick joyfully visited the big city. Now, he retreats to a dull but honest life in the country.
  (*The Great Gatsby*)

- Jake returns home to his wife, along with the money he hopes will convict Alonzo and clear himself. He sees news of Alonzo's murder (at the hands of the Russians) on TV, where Alonzo is being hailed as a hero. In the beginning, Jake would believed Alonzo's eulogy; now he will never believe such a thing again.
  (*Training Day*)

Name three ways you can contrast the Normal World from the beginning of the story with the new normal.

1. _____.

2. _____.

3. _____.

If it is possible for you to *physically* return your character to the Normal World,

how can you contrast the character's new self with the old world? _____

_____

_____.

EXAMPLE:

- An older, wiser Nick looks back on his adventures with Gatsby by ironically and a little contemptuously sharing some advice his father gave him: "Whenever you feel like criticizing any one [sic], just remember that all the people in this world haven't had the advantages you've had."

- At the beginning, Jake left his home clean, happy, and hopeful. He returns filthy, wounded, and heartbroken.

How will your Resolution answer the Thematic Question you asked in the first chapter? _____

_____.

EXAMPLE:

- **Thematic Question:** Will Jake embrace the idea that corruption is a necessary way of doing business for an effective detective?

- **Thematic Answer:** Yes, but he will refuse to compromise his own moral code any further, even at the risk of his own life.
  (*Training Day*)

How can you visually *show* the character's new thematic Truth without slapping readers in the face with the "moral of the story"? _____

_____

_____

_____.

How will your final scene be a downbeat one that demonstrates the broken dreams and ideals the protagonist was forced to sacrifice to a dark Truth he couldn't fully handle? _____

_____

_____

_____.

CREATIVE EXERCISE:

Consider how the Normal World of your story can best symbolize the Lie Your Character Believes, while the Adventure World proves (even if not on its surface) a contrary Truth.

SOMETHING TO THINK ABOUT:

1. How is the character devaluing the Truth in the beginning of the story?
2. Why does the Lie's Normal World appeal to the character?
3. How will your character fail in the story's end, even if he appears to gain an exterior victory of some sort?
4. Will supporting characters try to reason with your protagonist? How will he respond?

RESOURCES:

- "How to Create a Complex Moral Argument for Your Theme," helpingwritersbecomeauthors.com/create-complex-moral-argument-storys-theme
- "Are Happy Endings a Must?," helpingwritersbecomeauthors.com/are-happy-endings-must
- "How to Make Readers Love an Unlikable Character—And Hate a Likable One," helpingwritersbecomeauthors.com/how-to-make-readers-love-an-unlikable-character-and-hate-a-likable-one
- "Protagonist and Main Character—Same Person? The Answer May Transform Your Story!," helpingwritersbecomeauthors.com/protagonist-and-main-character-same-person-the-answer-may-transform-your-story
- "Would Your Story Benefit From a Distant Narrator?," helpingwritersbecomeauthors.com/would-your-story-benefit-from-distant

4

THE NEGATIVE
CHANGE ARC #2:
FALL

CHARACTER BELIEVES LIE > CLINGS TO LIE > REJECTS NEW TRUTH >
BELIEVES STRONGER/WORSE LIE

THE FALL ARC is the one we most commonly associate with tragedies. In this type of story, the character starts out just as he would in a Positive Change Arc: already entrenched in the Lie. But unlike a Positive Change Arc, in which he will eventually overcome the Lie and embrace the Truth, the protagonist in a Fall Arc will reject every chance for embracing a positive Truth and will fall more and more deeply into the morass of his own sins—usually dragging others right along with him. His story will end in insanity, oppressive immorality, or death.

NEGATIVE CHANGE ARC #2: FALL

CHARACTER BELIEVES LIE >
CLINGS TO LIE >
REJECTS NEW TRUTH >
BELIEVES WORSE LIE

THIRD ACT

100% — **Resolution** - Aftermath

98% — **Climactic Moment** - Total destruction

88% — **Climax** - Last-ditch attempt to salvage Want

75% — **3rd PLOT POINT** - Complete failure to gain either Want or Need

SECOND ACT

62% — **2nd Pinch Point** - Lie is effective, but destructive

50% — **MIDPOINT (2nd PLOT POINT)** - Moment of Truth : Glimpses Truth, rejects Truth, chooses worse Lie,

37% — **1st Pinch Point** - Halfhearted attempts at Truth only half-effective

FIRST ACT

25% — **1st PLOT POINT** - Lie now completely ineffective; makes a move toward Truth

12% — **Inciting Event** - First hint Lie will not save or reward

1% — **Hook** - Believes Lie

THE LIE YOUR CHARACTER BELIEVES

THE PROTAGONIST IN a Fall Arc will start out believing in a Lie that is holding him back. Just as in a Positive-Change and Disillusionment Arc, this Lie will be a fundamentally incorrect and damaging view of either the character and/or the world. Unlike in a Positive-Change Arc, however, the protagonist in a Fall Arc will look the Lie in the eyes and find himself unable to reject it in favor of a difficult but healing Truth. Instead, in his desperate attempts to survive, he will end by clinging to an even worse version of his original Lie.

(For more about the Lie Your Character Believes, see Chapters 1 and 18 in *Creating Character Arcs*.)

Write down four possible variations of the Lie Your Character Believes. Each one should be a specific belief, stated in one short sentence.

EXAMPLE:

- The orphaned Heathcliff starts out believing the Lie that in order to ever find personal wholeness or happiness, he must entirely possess his adopted sister, childhood sweetheart, and only friend Cathy Earnshaw. (*Wuthering Heights*)

- Sister Aloysius, the principal of a Catholic school, enters the story already believing the Lie that that faith and doubt cannot coexist. (*Doubt*)

Lie #1: _____

_____

_____.

Lie #2: _____

_____

_____.

Lie #3: _____

_____

_____.

Lie #4: _____

_____

_____.

How can each of these potential Lies be reflected in your character's exterior world and/or how can the exterior world be a metaphor for your character's inner struggle?

EXAMPLES:

- The harshness of Heathcliff's childhood is reflected in the harsh landscape of the moors and the very name of his home—Wuthering Heights—which describes "the atmospheric tumult to which its station is exposed in the stormy weather."
- Sister Aloysius lives in (and enforces) a strict, scheduled, and bleak parish, which is an explicit reflection of her own bleak black-and-white views.

Exterior World Reflection for Lie #1: _____

_____

_____

_____.

Exterior World Reflection for Lie #2: _____

_____

_____.

Exterior World Reflection for Lie #3: _____

_____

_____

_____.

Exterior World Reflection for Lie #4: _____

_____

_____

_____.

Which of these four Lies will be the primary Lie for your character's arc? Which one best influences your plot and theme?

       ☐ Lie #1
       ☐ Lie #2
       ☐ Lie #3
       ☐ Lie #4

Final Choice of the Lie Your Character Believes: _____

_____

_____

_____.

SYMPTOMS OF THE LIE

HAVING TROUBLE FINDING the Lie? Look for the "symptoms" of the Lie in the character's life by considering his actions and especially his reactions. None of these symptoms *are* the Lie, but they're often products of the Lie.

Your protagonist may be aware of the symptoms of the Lie in his life, even if he isn't yet able to recognize the Lie itself. More than that, he may want nothing more than to shed the negative symptoms, but he can't because he can't get past his fundamental belief in the Lie.

EXAMPLES:

- Marcus Annan's Lie is some sins are too great to be forgiven. His symptoms are guilt, shame, secrets, and a destructive lifestyle. (*Behold the Dawn*)

- Ebenezer Scrooge's Lie is a man's worth can only be measured by the amount of money he has earned. His symptoms are greed, cruelty, selfishness, and an inability to forgive. (*A Christmas Carol*)

Answer the following questions to further hone the right Lie for your story.

Which of the following symptoms are present in your character's life?

☐ Fear
How is it manifesting? _____

_____.

☐ Extreme hurt
How is it manifesting? _____

_____.

☐ Inability to forgive
How is it manifesting? _____

_____.

☐ Guilt
How is it manifesting? _____

_____.

☐ Horrible secrets

How is it manifesting? _____

_____.

☐ Shame over something the character did

How is it manifesting? _____

_____.

☐ Shame over something done *to* the character

How is it manifesting? _____

_____.

How is your character attempting to escape the pain caused by the symptoms of his

Lie? _____

_____

_____

_____

_____.

How is your character's inability to face the Lie trapping her within the painful symp-

toms despite her efforts to escape them? _____

_____

_____

_____

_____.

At the beginning of your story, what is your character lacking mentally, emotionally, or spiritually, as a result of the Lie? _____

_____

_____

_____.

In your first chapter, how can you dramatize what he is lacking and/or suffering as a result of his Lie? _____

_____

_____

_____

_____

_____.

YOUR CHARACTER'S GHOST

YOUR CHARACTER'S "GHOST" is something in his past that haunts him. You may also see it sometimes referred to as the "wound." This Ghost is the *reason* the character can't completely embrace the Truth and shrug off the Lie. Often, the wound will be something shocking and traumatic, but it can also be something small and ordinary, such as a stressful parental relationship or a physical inferiority.

(For more information about the Ghost, see Chapters 3 and 18 in *Creating Character Arcs*.)

Write down four possible events that might have happened in your character's past to traumatize him and/or motivate his belief in the Lie.

EXAMPLES:

- Heathcliff's Ghost is his own orphaned (and presumably illegitimate) childhood, in which he is endlessly spurned by everyone except Cathy and her father.
  (*Wuthering Heights*)

- We never get an explicit glimpse of Sister Aloysius's past, although she briefly mentions having been married.
  (*Doubt*)

Ghost #1: _____

_____

_____

_____.

Ghost #2: _____

_____

_____

_____.

Ghost #3: _____

_____

_____

_____.

Ghost #4: _____

_____

_____

_____.

Which of these four Ghosts will be the primary motivating wound in your character's backstory?

    ☐ Ghost #1
    ☐ Ghost #2
    ☐ Ghost #3
    ☐ Ghost #4

How has your chosen Ghost indirectly created or enabled the Lie Your Character

Believes? _____

_____.

How will the character use the Lie to try to compensate for, cover up, or simply

survive the consequences of the Ghost? _____

_____

_____.

How does the Ghost tie in thematically with the Lie? _____

_____

_____.

On a scale of 1 to 10, how "big" is the Ghost?

    1. ☐ (e.g., Stressful Parental Relationship)
    2. ☐
    3. ☐
    4. ☐
    5. ☐
    6. ☐
    7. ☐
    8. ☐
    9. ☐
    10. ☐ (e.g., Murder of a Loved One)

How is your Lie commensurate to the "size" of the Ghost (e.g., a big Ghost gets a big

Lie)? _____

_____

_____.

Must readers explicitly understand the Ghost in order for the rest of the story to make sense?

    ☐ Yes

    ☐ No

This Ghost will best be shared with readers how?

    ☐ As a mystery (teased in the beginning and revealed later at an important turning point in the plot)

    ☐ Dramatized at the beginning of the First Act

    ☐ Not shared at all

THE THING YOUR CHARACTER NEEDS

THE PROTAGONIST IN a Fall Arc desperately needs the Truth, right from the very beginning of her story. She is already suffering from her inability to get free from the Lie. The Thing She Needs is the Truth itself—the key to the door of the prison in which the Lie has kept her locked. Throughout the early part of the story, the character will struggle to try to find ways to accept and use the Truth, but she can never quite get her hands on it without releasing the Lie—which she refuses to do.

(For more information about the Thing Your Character Needs, see Chapters 2 and 18 in *Creating Character Arcs*.)

What Truth opposes the Lie Your Character Believes? _____

_____

_____.

EXAMPLE:

- Only once free of his obsessive and selfish adopted sister can Heathcliff have a chance of a whole and empowered life.
  (*Wuthering Heights*)

- Because faith and certainty cannot coexist, only by admitting and accepting doubt can faith be allowed to grow.
  (*Doubt*)

Write down four possible ways your story's Truth can manifest as a specific Thing Your Character Needs. This would be a specific action or belief on your character's part.

EXAMPLE:

- Recognize Cathy's destructive influence and leave her.

- Have faith in Father Flynn and give him the benefit of the doubt.

Thing Your Character Needs #1: _____

_____

_____.

Thing Your Character Needs #2: _____

_____

_____.

Thing Your Character Needs #3: _____

_____

_____.

Thing Your Character Needs #4: _____

_____

_____.

How might your character refuse to act upon each of these four options at the end of the story, to demonstrate her inability to understand or accept the Truth?

EXAMPLE:

- Heathcliff digs up Cathy's skeleton in order to be "with" her.
- Sister Aloysius lies about Father Flynn's past in order to drive him out of the parish.

Action based on Thing Your Character Needs #1: _____

_____

_____.

Action based on Thing Your Character Needs #2: _____

_____

_____.

Action based on Thing Your Character Needs #3: _____

_____

_____.

Action based on Thing Your Character Needs #4: _____

_____

_____.

Which of these four options will be the primary Thing Your Character Needs in this story? Which one best reflects your story's Truth?

☐ Thing Your Character Needs #1
☐ Thing Your Character Needs #2
☐ Thing Your Character Needs #3
☐ Thing Your Character Needs #4

Final Choice of the Thing Your Character Needs: _____

_____

_____.

How do you see the Truth manifesting externally/visually at the end of your story? _

_____

_____

_____.

THE THING YOUR CHARACTER WANTS

THE PROTAGONIST a Fall Arc is completely driven by the Thing He Wants. As the story progresses, it will consume him more and more, beyond morality, beyond reason. Deep down, he believes this desire is the key to exorcising his Ghost, healing his wounds, and making himself a whole person. What he fails to realize is that his obsessive focus on this external goal is, *at best*, a Band-Aid, incapable of fully healing him without the true power of the Truth. *At worst*, the Thing the Character Wants will be ultimately destructive in itself and will be the cause of the character's ruin in the end of the story.

(For more information about the Thing Your Character Wants, see Chapters 2 and 18 in *Creating Character Arcs*.)

Write down four possible Things Your Character Wants. These are deep primal desires. They are *not* necessarily your character's story goal, but they will influence the specific goal.

EXAMPLES:

- Marry Cathy.
  (*Wuthering Heights*)

- Remove Father Flynn from the parish.
  (*Doubt*)

Desire #1: _____

_____

_____.

Desire #2: _____

_____

_____.

Desire #3: _____

_____

_____.

Desire #4: _____

_____

_____.

How are each of these desires influenced by a symptom of the Lie?

Desire #1: _____

_____

_____.

Desire #2: _____

_____

_____.

Desire #3: _____

_____

_____.

Desire #4: _____

_____

_____.

What specific story goal arises from each of these desires? This will be the plot goal your character will be working toward over the course of your entire story.

EXAMPLE:

- Wreak vengeance on those who kept him away from Cathy.
- Investigate the possibility that Father Flynn is abusing a troubled choir boy.

Goal Arising From Desire #1: _____

_____

_____ .

Goal Arising From Desire #2: _____

_____

_____ .

Goal Arising From Desire #3: _____

_____

_____ .

Goal Arising From Desire #4: _____

_____

_____ .

Which of these four desires will be the primary Thing Your Character Wants in this story? Which one best guides your plot and theme?

☐ Desire #1
☐ Desire #2
☐ Desire #3
☐ Desire #4

Final Choice of the Thing Your Character Wants: _____

_____

_____.

Which of the four goals will be your character's primary plot goal in this story? Which one best represents the Thing He Wants and drives your plot?

- ☐ Goal #1
- ☐ Goal #2
- ☐ Goal #3
- ☐ Goal #4

Final Choice of Character's Plot Goal: _____

_____

_____

_____

_____

_____.

THE CHARACTERISTIC MOMENT

THE ACTUAL STRUCTURE of the character arc begins with the Characteristic Moment. The Characteristic Moment aligns with the structural Hook, which shows up the moment your protagonist does—presumably in the first chapter.

The Characteristic Moment is your protagonist's big debut. He steps onto the stage, the spotlight hits him—and he shines. In this one moment, he shows readers what he's all about: the good, the bad, and the worse to come. The Characteristic Moment shows readers exactly why this protagonist is going to be worth reading about.

(For more information about the Characteristic Moment, see Chapters 4 and 18 in *Creating Character Arcs*.)

EXAMPLE:

- The narrator first meets the antisocial Heathcliff at the end of his life, in the midst of his sullen and cowed household, when Heathcliff begrudges the narrator shelter.
  (*Wuthering Heights*)

- Sister Aloysius is introduced as she patrols the pews during Father Flynn's sermon, snapping at a sleeping child.
  (*Doubt*)

Before you can craft the perfect Characteristic Moment, you must first know something about your character. Answer the following questions for starters (and for a full character interview, see my books *Outlining Your Novel* and the *Outlining Your Novel Workbook*).

What is this character's role in the story?

☐ Protagonist

☐ Antagonist

☐ Mentor

☐ Sidekick

☐ Love Interest

☐ Other: _____

What is your character's name? _____.

How old is your character? _____.

Of what nationality is your character? _____.

What is your character's occupation or primary identity (e.g., stay-at-home mom, rebel

soldier)? _____

_____.

Does the character have any important physical characteristics (e.g., a limp, green

scales)? _____

_____.

Name three prevailing aspects of the character's personality (e.g., kindness, quick temper, wit):

    1. _____.

    2. _____.

    3. _____.

What *one* important personality trait, virtue, or skill best sums up your character? ____

_____

_____.

    How can you dramatize this aspect of your character to its fullest extent? ____

    _____.

How can you dramatize this aspect in a way that also introduces the plot? ____

_____

_____.

What do you want readers to find most sympathetic and/or interesting about this char-

acter? _____

_____.

How can you dramatize this aspect of your character in an opening scene? __

_____

_____.

What is your character's overall story goal and/or the Thing He Wants Most?_____

_____

_____.

How can you set up this goal or show the coming need for it in an opening

scene? _____

_____.

What is your character's scene goal in the opening chapter? _____

_____

_____

_____.

How will you dramatize this scene goal right from the start of your opening

scene? _____

_____.

How will the character's pursuit of this goal meet with an obvious obstacle (i.e.,

conflict)? _____

_____

_____.

How will this goal move the plot, either by immediately causing consequences

or setting them up for later? _____

_____

_____.

How can any of the above help you demonstrate, or at least hint at, your character's

Lie? _____

_____.

How can you craft the above elements to make your protagonist immediately appealing

to readers (e.g., what's keeping them from looking away?)?_____

_____

_____.

Which of your character's strengths can you show readers right away? _____

_____

_____

_____

_____
.

Which of your character's pertinent weaknesses (especially Lie-driven weaknesses)

can you show readers right away? _____

_____

_____

_____

_____.

List events or activities you can use in your opening chapter to dramatize all the of above. Try to think of "big" moments that are unique, visually engaging, and keep the characters in motion.

    1. _____.

    2. _____.

    3. _____.

    4. _____.

    5. _____.

Write a summary of your opening chapter and how you will introduce your character

in a memorable and engaging Characteristic Moment: _____

_____

_____

_____

_____

_____

_____

_____

_____

_____

_____

_____

_____

_____

Which of the following does your proposed Characteristic Moment accomplish?

- ☐ Introduce character.
- ☐ Reveal character's name.
- ☐ Indicate character's gender.
- ☐ Indicate character's age group.
- ☐ Indicate character's nationality.
- ☐ Indicate character's occupation/main identity.
- ☐ Indicate any important physical characteristics.
- ☐ Indicate role in the story (i.e., protagonist).
- ☐ Demonstrate prevailing aspect of personality.
- ☐ Hook readers' sympathy and/or interest.
- ☐ Demonstrate scene goal.
- ☐ Indicate story goal.
- ☐ Demonstrate (or at least hint at) Lie.
- ☐ Move plot directly or through foreshadowing.

If you're unable to combine the majority of the above elements into one scene, answer whether it would work better to divide the necessary characteristic elements into two or more scenes.

_____

_____

_____

_____

_____

_____.

THE NORMAL WORLD

THE CHARACTERISTIC MOMENT is only half of a good character arc's opening. It gives readers a character, but the character still needs context. The Normal World provides that context. At its most basic level, the Normal World is—as its name suggests—a setting. This is the place in which your story opens. It is a place in which your character is unhappy, but still complacent or apathetic in that unhappiness.

The Normal World plays a vital role in grounding the First Act of your story in a concrete setting. Even more important, the Normal World creates the standard against which all the personal and plot changes to come will be measured. Without this vivid opening example of what will change in your character's life, the rest of the arc will lack definition and potency.

(For more information about the Normal World, see Chapters 5 and 18 in *Creating Character Arcs*.)

EXAMPLE:

- Heathcliff's Normal World, at the start of his childhood at Wuthering Heights, is one of bleak prejudice and cruelty, in which everyone, including the servants, spurns and abuses him. Only Mr. Earnshaw and his daughter Cathy accept him.
  (*Wuthering Heights*)

- Sister Aloysius's world is one she largely controls—and upon which she has largely already inflicted her own Lie: a stark, gray parish, which she rules, as far as she dares, with an iron rod.
  (*Doubt*)

Briefly describe the physical setting of the Normal World (e.g., Chicago or Mars): __

_____.

How does your chosen Normal World symbolically represent the Lie Your Character

Believes? _____

_____.

EXAMPLE:

- Heathcliff's Normal World has taught him that Cathy—despite her own selfish temper—is the only person in the world who loves and accepts him. The blustery and bleak setting itself—the moors—are a potent visual metaphor for the character's inner landscape as well.

- Sister Aloysius's Normal World is built upon strict principles, which she interprets (and enforces) as leaving no room for doubt in anything, be it church services, discipline at the parochial school, or the behavior and beliefs of the new parish priest.

How will the Normal World visibly prove to readers (*show* them) your protagonist's

"before" state at the beginning of the story? _____

_____

_____

_____.

What setting for the Normal World provides the most logical backstory for *why* your

character believes the Lie? _____

_____

_____.

What is holding your protagonist in the Normal World that has kept him from leav-

ing it before now? _____

_____

_____.

How is your chosen Normal World initially empowering your character to continue believing his Lie by giving him no reason to look beyond it? _____

_____

_____

_____.

How will the Normal World contrast with the Adventure World that will follow in the next two acts? _____

_____

_____.

Which of the following will best describe the Adventure World of your story's main conflict?

☐   A dramatically new and different setting.

☐   The same physical setting as the Normal World, with only facets of the world changing.

When your protagonist is later forced out of the Normal World into the Second Act, how will this initially give him an opportunity to look past the Lie? _____

_____

_____

_____

_____.

THE FIRST ACT

WHERE DOES IT BELONG?

From the 1% mark to the 25% mark in your story.

THE THING THE Character Wants, the Thing He Needs, and the Ghost will be basically the same in both a Fall Arc and a Positive Change Arc. It's only how the character deals with his Ghost over the course of the story that significantly differs—as he falls prey to its power over him, rather than overcoming it.

(For more information about the First Act in a Fall Arc, see Chapter 18 in *Creating Character Arcs*.)

How will you reinforce/dramatize the character's initial Lie? _____

_____

_____

_____.

How will you prove how the character's external problems are, in turn, causing internal

problems? _____

_____

_____.

How will you demonstrate the Thing Your Character Wants and the Thing She

Needs? _____

_____

_____.

How will her Characteristic Moment illustrate or hint at the Lie? _____

_____

_____

_____

_____.

How will her Normal World immediately illustrate or hint at the Lie? _____

_____

_____

_____

_____.

Name three ways you will continue to reinforce the Lie or introduce more of its facets throughout the First Act:

1. _____.

2. _____.

3. _____.

How can you hint at your character's latent capability for even greater darkness? ___

_____

_____

_____.

EXAMPLE:

- Heathcliff's violent nature causes him to lash out at others, even as a boy.
- After hearing Father Flynn's sermon on the acceptability of doubt, Sister Aloysius ironically begins to sow doubt amongst the other sisters by suggesting all has not been well at the parochial school since his arrival.

What specific character trait will be intrinsic to your character's inability to fight his

way out of the Lie? _____

_____.

Even if this trait isn't yet fully developed, how can you hint right from the begin-

ning that the seed is present? _____

_____.

How can you begin giving the character small hints about the destructive nature of the

Lie and the positive nature of the Truth? _____

_____

_____

_____.

What Inciting Event will be the Call to Adventure that first brushes your character

against the main conflict? _____

_____

_____.

- Cathy begins to disdain Heathcliff's devotion after she gets a taste of a more refined world while convalescing with the neighboring Lintons. She begins to accept Edgar Linton's romantic advances much to Heathcliff's despair.

- On Monday, as school begins, Sister Aloysius observes Father Flynn's friendliness with the children, especially the boys, one of whom pulls away from him. That evening, she questions the other nuns about his sermon the previous day and warns them to be on guard.

How will this Inciting Event set up the character's entry into the Adventure World

of the main conflict in the Second Act? _____

_____

_____

_____.

Does the Inciting Event initially seem:

☐ a good thing.

☐ a bad thing.

How will the Call to Adventure initially be met with resistance or refusal? _____

_____

_____.

EXAMPLE:

- Heathcliff loathes the Lintons and disdains everything to do with them, demanding Cathy come back to him.

- The other nuns, particularly the naïve and goodhearted Sister James, react with blank confusion to Sister Aloysius's subtle aspersions against Father Flynn.

Will the protagonist be the one to initially reject the Call to Adventure, or will someone else try to reject it for him? _____

_____.

How long will it take the protagonist to stop resisting?

☐ Entire rest of the First Act up to the First Plot Point.

☐ Shorter period ending with what event _____.

How does the Inciting Event change the protagonist's awareness of and comparative apathy about the Normal World in however small or subconscious a way? _____

_____

_____

_____.

How will your protagonist still be entrenched in the Lie toward the end of the First Act? _____

_____

_____.

How will his subconscious attitude toward the positivity of the Truth take a small step forward?_____

_____

_____.

What will the protagonist decide to *do* about the Call to Adventure at the Inciting

Event? _____

_____

_____

_____

_____.

THE FIRST PLOT POINT

WHERE DOES IT BELONG?

25% of the way into your story.

BECAUSE NEGATIVE CHANGE Arcs are about a descent into darkness, they must begin in a place high enough for the story to descend *from*. As a result, the First Plot Point will frequently be a positive one. Something seemingly good or interesting happens to the character. He meets the girl of his dreams; he gets a new job; he escapes from a bad situation. He may even make a good decision, one with the potential to lead him *away* from his Lie.

(For more information about the First Plot Point in a Fall Arc, see Chapter 19 in *Creating Character Arcs*.)

What event occurs at the end of the First Act that causes your character to leave the

Normal World and irreversibly begin pursuing his main story goal? _____

_____

_____

_____.

EXAMPLE:

- After Cathy accepts Edgar's marriage proposal, Heathcliff silently leaves, determined to make something of his life so he can return to marry Cathy himself. His decision is an entirely positive one. He wants to rise above his circumstances, leave behind the tyranny of Cathy's brother Hindley, and claim Cathy's hand as an equal.
  (*Wuthering Heights*)

- Uncertain how to interpret Father Flynn's relationship with a young boy named Donald, Sister James comes to Sister Aloysius, who immediately assumes the worst and sets out to convict and defrock Father Flynn.
  (*Doubt*)

In what way might this event be surprising even after the Inciting Event? _____

_____

_____.

Which of the following best describes your First Plot Point?

☐   A seemingly positive opportunity.

☐   Something disastrous.

What decision on your character's part led him right up to the First Plot Point, making

him at least partially responsible for what happens? _____

_____

_____.

EXAMPLE:

- Heathcliff's own rude manners and defiance, especially in the Lintons' presence, has proven what Cathy calls his "lowness," which is her chief reason for rejecting a romantic relationship with him.

- Sister Aloysius instructs Sister James to come to her with any suspicions she might have about Father Flynn—sowing suspicion to begin with.

Which of the following best describes your First Plot Point?

☐   It destroys the Normal World, leaving the protagonist no choice but to move on.

☐   It physically removes the protagonist from the Normal World.

☐   It warps the Normal World, forcing the protagonist to adapt to new ways of surviving within it.

Which best describes your protagonist's reaction to the First Plot Point?

☐   Enthusiasm—she wants to enter the conflict of the Second Act.

☐   Resistance—she has to be forced to enter the conflict of the Second Act.

After the First Plot Point, how will your protagonist react? _____

_____

_____

_____

_____.

What definitive action will he take to move forward into the Adventure World of

the main conflict? _____

_____

_____.

Which will the character be trying to do?

☐   Restore the old normal.

How: _____.

☐   Find a new normal.

How: _____.

Name three new physical needs that must be met in the aftermath of the First Plot
Point:

1. _____.

2. _____.

3. _____.

What definitive new plot goal will the character now adopt (something quantifiable,

based on the Thing He Wants)? _____

_____

_____

_____.

Do you want the character to ultimately achieve this goal?

☐　Yes.
　　Why? _____.

☐　No.
　　Why? _____.

How will the character's decisions and actions in the aftermath of the First Plot Point

give her the opportunity to overcome the Lie, while also sowing seeds for an even worse

manifestation of the Lie yet to come? _____

_____

_____

_____

.

What about the Adventure World of the Second Act makes the character's initial Lie less

comfortable than it was in the Normal World? _____

_____

_____.

THE FIRST HALF OF THE SECOND ACT

WHERE DOES IT BELONG?

From the 25% mark to the 50% mark in your story.

AS ALWAYS, THE First Half of the Second Act is all about the character's reaction to the First Plot Point. In a Fall Arc, he will be getting a full-on lesson in the Truth in this section. He's going to be suffering as a result of continuing to believe in and use the Lie. He's not getting the Thing He Wants because his methods are flawed, and, what's more, he's getting slapped for even trying. Even though he will have moments when he rethinks his devotion to the Lie, he wants his story goal too badly to let it go.

(For more information about the First Half of the Second Act in a Fall Arc, see Chapter 19 in *Creating Character Arcs*.)

How can other characters *show* your protagonist the Truth, rather than just *telling* her

about it? _____

_____

_____

_____.

How will your protagonist consider and perhaps even attempt these approaches to the Truth, while still being held back by her Lie?_____

_____

_____

_____.

How is your protagonist feeling slightly out of place within the new Adventure World

of the Second Act? _____

_____

_____.

EXAMPLE:

- Heathcliff returns to Wuthering Heights as a gentleman, but is still treated badly by Hindley and even Cathy.
  (*Wuthering Heights*)

What Lie-based actions is the protagonist continuing to use to try to reach his goals?

_____

_____.

How are these old Lie-based actions proving less effective in the Second Act than

they did in the First? _____

_____

_____.

EXAMPLE:

- Even though Heathcliff has returned a gentleman, no longer subject to his adopted family (thanks to the Truth—which allowed him to separate himself from Cathy, however briefly), he still can't shake the eerie obsession that binds him to his cruel adopted sister, sometimes even against his will.

- Sister Aloysius pursues the matter of Father Flynn's relationship with Donald, only to meet with resistance from others, who insist she has no real proof beyond her own certainty.
  (*Doubt*)

How is the protagonist demonstrating confusion or frustration about why his

original Lie is no longer working so well for him? _____

_____

_____.

What first move will he make to slowly begin evolving his tactics to avoid his Lie-

based failures so far? _____

_____

_____.

How can he initially consider the Truth as a solution, while also sliding even

deeper into a worse version of his Lie? _____

_____

_____.

How is the character pursuing the Thing She Wants in the Second Act? _____

_____

_____.

How is she getting closer to achieving her plot goal? _____

_____

_____.

How is her pursuit of the Thing She Wants pushing her away from the Thing She

Needs? _____

_____

_____

_____.

If the character continues down this path unchecked, what personal, spiritual,

and perhaps even physical destruction would she end up running into? _____

_____

_____

_____.

EXAMPLE:

- After Cathy marries Edgar, Heathcliff continues to cling to her, even though part of him hates her for being untrue to both him and herself. His dark nature comes swarming out as he begins enacting his vengeance against Hindley (by encouraging his gambling and drinking) and against Edgar (by marrying his sister Isabella).
- Sister Aloysius's pursuit of certainty increasingly undermines what remains of her own tottering faith.

How can you give your character a tiny glimpse of what life would be like were he to

abandon the Lie and seek the Truth instead? _____

_____

_____.

THE MIDPOINT

WHERE DOES IT BELONG?

50% of the way into your story.

THE MIDPOINT IS where it all changes. Up to this point, the character has been advancing toward his Lie, but the advance has been slow—and certainly not irreversible. He's had *at least* a few moments where he's been torn about the course he's following. But at the Midpoint, he takes an irremediable action or experiences a blindingly clear revelation that will see him launching himself into the second half with a series of strong Lie-based actions.

(For more information about the Midpoint in a Fall Arc, see Chapter 19 in *Creating Character Arcs*.)

What is your story's Midpoint event? _____

_____

_____.

EXAMPLE:

- Cathy dies in childbirth.
  (*Wuthering Heights*)

- Sister Aloysius confronts Father Flynn, who explains the situation by revealing he has been trying to protect Donald's status as an altar boy after he was caught drinking communion wine. Even though there is no obvious reason to doubt his word, Sister Aloysius determines to "bring him down."
  (*Doubt*)

What can you do to make this centerpiece scene as "big" as possible? _____

_____

_____

_____.

How have the events of the First Half of the Second Act led up to the Midpoint by drawing your protagonist away from the hope represented by the Truth? _____

_____

_____

_____.

How will the external events of the Midpoint prompt a "Moment of Truth," in which the character sees the benefits of the Truth but cannot bring himself to embrace it? _____

_____

_____.

What worse manifestation of his Lie will he embrace instead? _____

_____

_____.

EXAMPLE:

- With Cathy now forcibly removed from his life, Heathcliff is given the opportunity to accept the Truth that he's better off without her. But he not only throws aside this Truth, he embraces a new and more horrible Lie: he would rather have Cathy's ghost haunt him and drive him insane than give her up.

- Even though she has little grounds for a case against Father Flynn (which provides her the opportunity to evolve her doubt in him to faith), Sister Aloysius immediately rejects his innocence, determined to convict Father Flynn, with or without proof.

How will the events of the Midpoint act as a swivel between the two halves of your story—shifting your character out of uninformed reaction and into educated action?

_____

_____

_____.

In the second half of the story, how will the character use this radical new Lie to force his way toward the Thing He Wants—but in a destructive manner? _____

_____

_____

_____.

Even as he makes progress toward his plot goal, how will the character continue to be "punished" for his Lie-based actions in a way that prevents him from achieving total victory while still in the Second Act? _____

_____

_____

_____.

THE SECOND HALF OF THE SECOND ACT

WHERE DOES IT BELONG?

From the 50% mark to the 75% mark in your story.

THE TRAGIC PREMISE of the Fall Arc indicates a progression from bad to worse in the Second Half of the Second Act. Whatever the character's Lie in the beginning, he will now begin growing into its worst manifestation. If he fought lust in the story's beginning, he will now descend into adultery or even rape. If he struggled with hatred, he may end up plotting a murder.

(For more information about the Second Half of the Second Act in a Fall Arc, see Chapter 19 in *Creating Character Arcs*.)

How is the character acting on the worse Lie she embraced at the Midpoint? _____

_____

_____.

What new (but destructive) "tools" did the worse Lie provide your character that are

allowing him to make better progress toward the Thing He Wants? _____

_____

_____.

What obstacles will the antagonistic force still be putting in his way? _____

_____

_____

_____.

EXAMPLE:

- After Cathy's death, Heathcliff lashes out in anger, punishing everyone who had anything to do with keeping him away from her. He coerces his adopted brother Hindley into drunken gambling that allows Heathcliff to gain the deed to Wuthering Heights—and then he aids Hindley in drinking himself to death. He shows no care for his own pregnant wife—Isabella Linton—and lets her flee to another town. He raises Hindley's son Hareton in as abject degradation as he himself was raised. And as the years go by, he plots to marry his sickly son Linton to Edgar and Cathy's daughter Catherine, so he can gain control of a dying Edgar's property as well.
(*Wuthering Heights*)

- Sister Aloysius pursues her goal of casting Father Flynn out of the parish, regardless of any moral or sensible grounds. She takes her accusations to the boy's mother, even in the face of the mother's revelations about abuse the boy suffers at home and pleas that he not be removed from the prestigious church school.
(*Doubt*)

How is the Truth still present in the character's life, if only on a subconscious level? _

_____

_____

_____.

Name four destructive consequences the character's Lie-driven mindset and actions are having on the world and characters around him:

1. _____.

2. _____.

3. _____.

4. _____.

Name the destructive consequences the character's Lie-driven mindset and actions are having on himself:

Mentally: _____.

Emotionally: _____.

Physically: _____.

Spiritually: _____.

How is the character in more desperate need than ever of the Thing She Needs—

even though she won't admit it? _____

_____.

Write down four scenes from the first half of the story in which your character demonstrated his original Lie-driven motives. Then brainstorm four scenes you can include in the second half that will contrast the earlier scenes by showing how your character's new and worse Lie has already started to change him.

"Before" Scenes

1. _____

2. _____

3. _____

4. _____

"After" Scenes

1. _____

2. _____

3. _____

4. _____

EXAMPLE:

- **Before:** Heathcliff hated and resisted his cruel brother-in-law Hindley, but still subjected himself to Hindley's punishments.
- **After:** Heathcliff does everything he can to destroy Hindley—winning away his property in card games and goading Hindley into drinking himself to death.

At the end of the Second Act, how will the Thing the Character Wants place itself within

the character's grasp, offering a seeming victory? _____

_____

_____

_____.

Example:

- Heathcliff enacts the last piece of his plotted vengeance by kidnapping Edgar and Cathy's teenage daughter Catherine and refusing to let her return to her dying father unless she marries Heathcliff's son Linton (thus giving Heathcliff Edgar's property as well as Hindley's).
- When confronted by Father Flynn, Sister Aloysius insists his past proves his troubling nature, since he has moved to three different parishes in the last five years. He is unable to change her convictions and leaves, defeated.

How must the character utterly subject himself to the worse Lie in order to claim the

Thing He Wants? _____

_____

_____.

How will the character entirely sacrifice the Thing He Needs in order to gain the

Thing He Wants at this point? _____

_____

_____

_____.

How does the character justify this to himself? _____

_____

_____

_____

_____.

THE THIRD PLOT POINT

WHERE DOES IT BELONG?

75% of the way into your story.

IN ONE WORD, the Fall Arc is about *failure*. This becomes nowhere more clear than at the Third Plot Point. Although still symbolic of death, the Third Plot Point in a Fall Arc brings the character not to his greatest defeat yet—but to his greatest triumph. Or so it seems. He has used his great Lie to conquer within the exterior plot, but the victory is utterly empty and comes at the cost of his soul.

(For more information about the Third Plot Point in a Fall Arc, see Chapter 20 in *Creating Character Arcs*.)

What Third Plot Point crisis will bring your protagonist to an exterior victory that

wreaks havoc on the world and characters around him? _____

_____

_____

_____.

EXAMPLE:

- Heathcliff achieves his great end—as many tragic protagonists do—by completing his vengeance. He has destroyed Edgar: his enemy is dead, and Heathcliff now holds title to all his property, via the forced marriage of Edgar's daughter to Heathcliff's son. But Heathcliff's victory has brought him no closer to peace—or to his true goal of being with Cathy. In the aftermath of his triumph, life is emptier than ever. (*Wuthering Heights*)

- Sister Aloysius succeeds is expelling Father Flynn from the parish, leaving Sister James feeling guilty and in doubt, and the boy Donald visibly upset. (*Doubt*)

How do other characters react to what the protagonist does at the Third Plot Point?

_____

_____.

How will some of your supporting characters demonstrate the better road the

protagonist might have walked had he chosen the Truth here? _____

_____

_____.

How will other supporting characters demonstrate their own negative descent as

a result of the protagonist's influence? _____

_____

_____.

How does the Third Plot Point definitively prove the protagonist's choice between

the Thing She Wants and the Thing She Needs by forcing her to sacrifice the latter?

_____

_____.

How can you make the rejection of the Truth as painful as possible? _____

_____

_____.

How can you contrast the healing power of the Truth with the greater tempta-

tion of the victory the Lie promises at this point? _____

_____

_____

_____.

How can you cast the pall of death over the Third Plot Point by featuring it either

literally or symbolically? _____

_____

_____

_____.

EXAMPLE:

- Heathcliff uses Edgar's incumbent death to pressure Catherine into a living hell—selling herself and all her property into his power by marrying Linton.
- Sister Aloysius's successful campaign against Father Flynn is an assassination of his character, a symbolic death of the life he currently lives in her parish.

THE FIRST HALF OF THE THIRD ACT

WHERE DOES IT BELONG?

From the 75% mark to the 88% mark in your story.

AFTER THE BREAKING point at the Third Plot Point, the tragic hero will rage futilely against death and its power, rather than rising into a personal resurrection. He simply has too much invested in his present course; he can't afford to admit how wrong he has been, even at the cost of alienating those he would previously have fought and died for. His dark ends are entirely outweighing the means they cost to achieve.

(For more information about the First Half of the Third Act in a Fall Arc, see Chapter 20 in *Creating Character Arcs*.)

How can you up the stakes after the Third Plot Point by emphasizing the emptiness

of your protagonist's victory? _____

_____

_____

_____.

Will the character have reason to at least momentarily regret his decision to abandon

the Truth? _____

_____

_____

_____.

How will your character try to block his pain with the conviction that he made the

only possible choice and that the Thing He Wants is worth the price? _____

_____

_____.

EXAMPLE:

- After the completion of his vengeance against Edgar, Heathcliff sinks deeper and deeper into despair. He is broken, and he can't find the strength to rise above his continuing obsessive need to be with Cathy. He even goes so far as to dig up her long-rotted corpse, and he does find momentary peace in the belief it will be his soul—and not Edgar's—that will reunite with her in death. (*Wuthering Heights*)

- After Father Flynn's expulsion, Sister Aloysius tries to bolster herself with a self-righteous insistence that she did the right thing. (*Doubt*)

Even after your character fully claims the Lie, how can you keep him off-balance by

forcing him to look at how life would have been better with the Truth? _____

_____

_____.

Name four ways it is becoming increasingly difficult for the character to maintain sanity and centeredness amidst the consequences and continuing progress of his Lie:

1. _____.

2. _____.

3. _____.

4. _____.

How is your character different in the Third Act from who he was in the First Act? _

_____

_____

_____.

How can you demonstrate this by giving your protagonist the opportunity to symbolically reject the wholeness offered by the Truth in a physical way? ___

_____

_____

_____.

EXAMPLE:

- After his own son dies, Heathcliff drifts through life, torturing Edgar's daughter Catherine and Hindley's son Hareton—in whom he sees an eerie resemblance of his own youthful relationship with Cathy. He believes Cathy's ghost has finally returned to haunt him. The only possible remaining route to joining her is death itself.

- When Father Flynn asks Sister Aloysius, "Where is your compassion?", she scoffs at him: "Nowhere you can get at it."

Prior to the Climax, how can you use a minor character to try to convince the protagonist

to finally abandon the Lie? _____

_____

_____

_____.

- Heathcliff visits Nelly Dean, a servant from his childhood home, and tells her about digging up Cathy's corpse. Nelly—although not in the least sympathetic to Heathcliff's motives and means—tries to advise him he is on a path to destruction. But he will not be swayed. He knows he is on a path to destruction, but he believes it is inescapable.

THE CLIMAX

WHERE DOES IT BELONG?

From the 88% mark to the 98% mark in your story.

THE CLIMAX IN a Fall Arc will progress with an overwhelming sense of inevitable destruction. The character has already fully and irretrievably sold himself to the worst possible incarnation of his Lie. His fate is sealed; he cannot turn back. He knows this at least on a subconscious level, and probably even on a conscious level. But he thrusts away any remaining doubts or fears and pushes forward, hell-bent on gaining the Thing He Wants. He has come too far and sacrificed too much not to give the last full measure in obtaining it here.

(For more information about the Climax in a Fall Arc, see Chapter 20 in *Creating Character Arcs*.)

What one moment have readers been waiting for since the beginning of the story? _

_____

_____.

How can you deliver this moment? _____

_____

_____.

How has your character recently proven *before* the Climax that she will do anything

she must to reach her goal? _____

_____

_____.

What form will the final confrontation between the protagonist and the antagonistic

force take? _____

_____.

EXAMPLES:

- Naval battle.
  (*Master and Commander*)

- Horse race.
  (*The Reivers*)

- Filibuster.
  (*Mr. Smith Goes to Washington*)

Where will your Climax take place? _____.

> How does this setting symbolically emphasize the central conflict and the
>
> theme? _____
>
> _____.
>
> How does this setting physically or emotionally make the confrontation with the
>
> antagonist more difficult? _____
>
> _____.

How is the nature of the final climactic confrontation perfectly suited to provide the

final test for your protagonist's new Lie, absolutely proving her devotion to it?

_____

_____.

How will the antagonistic force attempt to use the Truth to change the protagonist's mind one last time—and fail? _____

_____

_____

_____.

How will the protagonist attempt to use her new Lie to overcome the antagonistic force and remove the last obstacle between herself and her main plot goal? _

_____

_____

_____.

Do you want the protagonist to achieve his plot goal and gain the Thing He Wants?

Why? _____

_____

_____.

If the protagonist fails in reaching his goal, how will he react to his utter defeat? _____

_____

_____.

If the protagonist succeeds in reaching his goal, how will he react to its comparative emptiness? _____

_____

_____

_____.

Will your protagonist die in the Climactic Moment?

☐ Yes
☐ No

How will your Climactic Moment emphasize, either blatantly or ironically, the utter futility of the character's Lie? _____

_____

_____.

EXAMPLE:

- Heathcliff pursues Cathy's ghost on the moors at night. His health declines and, finally, in a hectic state of joy, believing he will be reunited with her, he dies.
  (*Wuthering Heights*)

- Father Flynn preaches a final sermon of farewell, in which he reveals that, despite his sadness and defeat in leaving his congregation (who have no idea why he's leaving), he maintains his hope and faith in life. Sister Aloysius has achieved her goal in removing him from the parish, but she was unable to destroy him.
  (*Doubt*)

THE RESOLUTION

WHERE DOES IT BELONG?

From the 98% mark to the 100% mark in your story.

THE ENDING SCENES in a tragedy are often comparatively short. Unlike a positive story, Fall Arcs leave few loose ends and don't usually inspire in readers a desire to stick around in the story world. The great tragedy in the Climax is underscored with a sense of finality that doesn't require much mopping up.

(For more information about the Resolution in a Fall Arc, see Chapter 20 in *Creating Character Arcs*.)

Now that the plot goal has proved itself utterly unworthy of the sacrifices the pro-

tagonist made, how is she able to face the future? _____

_____

_____.

How will the available choices for her new life moving forward contrast with

the choices she was offered back in the first chapter? _____

_____

_____.

If your protagonist died in the Climax, how can you indicate what will happen to the surviv-

ing characters moving forward? _____

_____

_____.

Name three ways you can contrast the Normal World from the beginning of the story with the new normal.

1. _____.

2. _____.

3. _____.

If it is possible for you to *physically* return your characters to the Normal World,

how can you contrast their new selves with the old world? _____

_____

_____

_____

_____.

How will your Resolution answer the Thematic Question you asked in the first chap-

ter?_____

_____

_____

_____.

EXAMPLE:

- **Thematic Question:** Can an unhealthy and obsessive devotion to a self-ish person ever bring personal happiness and empowerment?
- **Thematic Answer:** No, it leads to jealousy, bitterness, hatred, insanity, and death.

How can you visually *show* the consequences of the character's Lie without slapping readers in the face with the "moral of the story"? _____

_____

_____

_____.

EXAMPLE:

- Heathcliff's death is proof in itself. He destroyed his own life and those of everyone around him.
  (*Wuthering Heights*)

Do you wish to end the story on a downbeat note emphasizing the horror of the Lie or an upbeat note emphasizing the latent restorative power of the Truth? _____

_____

_____.

EXAMPLE:

- Without Heathcliff's dark presence to poison their lives, Catherine and Hareton begin at last to bring love and happiness back into the corrupted atmosphere of Wuthering Heights. The book closes on an entirely hopeful note, promising the end of suffering. There's even a hint of hope for Heathcliff, as the old manservant insists he can see his master's ghost walking the moors with Cathy. The narrator, however, gives his own spin on a hopeful end for Heathcliff, believing that in death, at least, he will find rest.

- Even after revealing she lied about the proof she previously said she collected about Father Flynn, Sister Aloysius adamantly adheres to her belief in his guilt. And yet she is not at peace. In the final moments of the story, she breaks down and admits a crisis of faith to Sister James: "I have doubts. I have such doubts."
  (*Doubt*)

CREATIVE EXERCISE:

The Fall Arc is about the character progressing from one Lie to a worse Lie. Brainstorm a list of increasingly "worse" Lies the character might embrace if he starts down that path.

SOMETHING TO THINK ABOUT:

1. How is the character already entrenched in the Lie's Normal World? Why has he not yet made a move to escape this Normal World?
2. How will your character suffer for his devotion to the Lie?
3. How will his actions irrevocably damage others?
4. What less-than-ideal (and possibly even downright evil) plan will your protagonist come up with for confronting the antagonistic force and gaining the Thing He Wants?

RESOURCES:

- "Want a Powerful Theme for Your Novel? Play Devil's Advocate!," helpingwritersbecomeauthors.com/powerful-theme-2
- "How to Make Readers Happy by Giving Them Exactly What They Don't Want," helpingwritersbecomeauthors.com/how-to-make-readers-happy-by-giving-them-exactly-what-they-dont-want
- "Should You Give Your Characters Unlikable Traits?," helpingwritersbecomeauthors.com/should-give-your-characters-unlikable
- "How to Be a Gutsy Writer: Stay True to Your Characters," helpingwritersbecomeauthors.com/writer-stay-true-to-your-characters
- "4 Ways to Make Your Antihero Deliciously Irresistible," helpingwritersbecomeauthors.com/4-ways-to-make-your-antihero

5
THE NEGATIVE CHANGE ARC #3:
CORRUPTION

CHARACTER SEES TRUTH > REJECTS TRUTH > EMBRACES LIE

IN A CORRUPTION Arc, the character starts out in a world that already knows and embraces the Truth. He has every opportunity to do the same, but is lured away by the Lie. Just as the seed of the Truth is already latent in the life of a Positive Change Arc character, the seed of the Lie is latent in the Corruption Arc character—even though the Truth is already right in front of him. This is perhaps the most moving of all the arcs, since it features a character who is good—or at least has a great potential for goodness—but who throws away that chance and consciously chooses darkness.

NEGATIVE CHANGE ARC #3: CORRUPTION

CHARACTER SEES TRUTH >
REJECTS TRUTH >
EMBRACES LIE

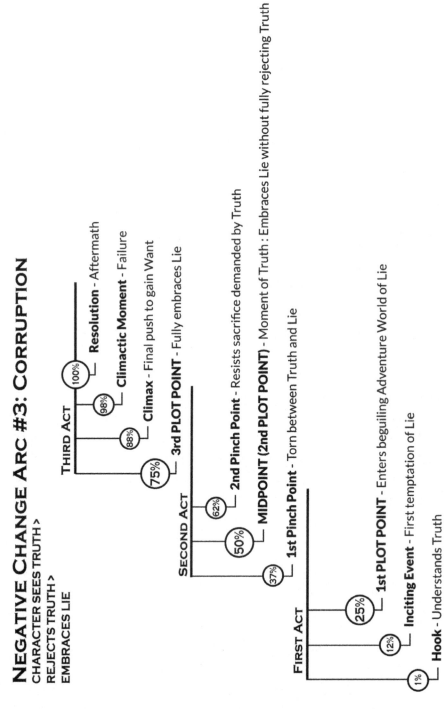

THIRD ACT

100% Resolution - Aftermath

98% Climactic Moment - Failure

88% Climax - Final push to gain Want

75% 3rd PLOT POINT - Fully embraces Lie

SECOND ACT

62% 2nd Pinch Point - Resists sacrifice demanded by Truth

50% MIDPOINT (2nd PLOT POINT) - Moment of Truth : Embraces Lie without fully rejecting Truth

37% 1st Pinch Point - Torn between Truth and Lie

FIRST ACT

25% 1st PLOT POINT - Enters beguiling Adventure World of Lie

12% Inciting Event - First temptation of Lie

1% Hook - Understands Truth

THE TRUTH YOUR CHARACTER BELIEVES

I N A CORRUPTION Arc, the Lie the Character Believes will eventually end up being about something the character *already* possesses but devalues (e.g., he's already filthy rich, but he fails to value or be responsible with his blessings). What he ends up devaluing is, at its heart, the Truth. No matter what other negative circumstances in the character's life, there will be at least one specific, objectively good thing (the Truth) that he will take for granted in the beginning. Worse, by the end of the story, he will be willing to sacrifice this good Truth in order to pursue the false promise of the Lie

(For more information about the Truth Your Character Believes in a Corruption Arc, see Chapter 18 in *Creating Character Arcs*.)

Write down four possible variations of the Truth Your Character Believes. Each one should be a specific belief, stated in one short sentence.

EXAMPLE:

- Anakin Skywalker starts out as an optimistic, hopeful child who brings light and kindness into the lives of all those around him. The Truth he already knows is that love is stronger than physical power.
(*Star Wars*)

- Michael Corleone begins as an upstanding man who rejects his Mafia family's corruption and violence as a clearly wrong and ultimately undesirable means to an end.
(*The Godfather*)

Truth #1: _____

_____.

Truth #2: _____

_____

_____.

Truth #3: _____

_____

_____.

Truth #4: _____

_____

_____.

Which of these four Truths will be the primary Truth for your story? Which one best influences your plot and theme?

    ☐ Truth #1
    ☐ Truth #2
    ☐ Truth #3
    ☐ Truth #4

What major Lie will eventually stand in opposition to your protagonist's Truth? _____

_____

_____.

EXAMPLE:

- The seed of the Lie is already within Anakin, even as a child: the ability to impose one's will upon others is the greatest and most important power in the world.

- Michael's desire for normalcy beyond his crime family's lifestyle is contrasted with his equally strong devotion to his father and siblings, hinting he will eventually succumb to the Lie that defending one's family is an end that justifies all means.

YOUR CHARACTER'S GHOST

YOUR CHARACTER'S "GHOST" is something in his past that haunts him. You may also see it sometimes referred to as the "wound." This Ghost is the *reason* the character can't completely embrace the Truth and shrug off the Lie. Often, the wound will be something shocking and traumatic, but it can also be something small and ordinary, such as a stressful parental relationship or a physical inferiority. The bigger and more destructive the Lie, the more shocking and impactful the Ghost should be. Or to flip that on its head: the bigger the Ghost, the bigger the Lie, the bigger the arc.

(For more information about the Ghost, see Chapters 3 and 18 in *Creating Character Arcs*.)

Write down four possible events that might have happened in your character's past to traumatize him and/or provide the initial seeds for the Lie that is already latent within your character.

EXAMPLES:

- The seed of Anakin's Lie is already within him, fertilized by his Ghost as a repressed and powerless slave.
(*Star Wars*)

- Michael's backstory is never explicitly explored, but we understand he was obviously raised in the heart of a crime family, by a crime lord father whom he loved in no small part because the man wanted better things for him and encouraged him to go straight rather than join the family business.
(*The Godfather*)

Ghost #1: _____

_____.

Ghost #2: _____

_____

_____.

Ghost #3: _____

_____

_____.

Ghost #4: _____

_____

_____.

Which of these four Ghosts will be the primary motivating wound in your character's backstory?

☐ Ghost #1
☐ Ghost #2
☐ Ghost #3
☐ Ghost #4

How will your chosen Ghost indirectly create or enable the Lie Your Character

Believes? _____

_____

_____.

How is the character currently able to use the Truth to salve the wound of the

Ghost? _____

_____

_____

_____.

Later in the story, as the character moves away from the Truth, how will he use the Lie to try to compensate for, cover up, or simply survive the consequences of the Ghost? _____

_____

_____.

How does the Ghost tie in thematically with the Lie? _____

_____

_____.

On a scale of 1 to 10, how "big" is the Ghost?
 1. ☐ (e.g., Stressful Parental Relationship)
 2. ☐
 3. ☐
 4. ☐
 5. ☐
 6. ☐
 7. ☐
 8. ☐
 9. ☐
10. ☐ (e.g., Murder of a Loved One)

How is your Lie (and thus the degree of change your character must undergo) commensurate to the "size" of the Ghost (e.g., a big Ghost gets a big Lie)? _____

_____

_____.

Must readers explicitly understand the Ghost in order for the rest of the story to make sense?

       ☐ Yes

       ☐ No

This Ghost will best be shared with readers how?

       ☐ As a mystery (teased in the beginning and revealed later at an important turning point in the plot)

       ☐ Dramatized at the beginning of the First Act

       ☐ Not shared at all

THE THING YOUR CHARACTER WANTS

THE PROTAGONIST IN a Corruption Arc will slowly become more and more consumed by the Thing He Wants. This desire—driven by the unresolved Ghost in his past—will start out as only a restless niggle in the beginning of the story. But as the character begins to see an opportunity to claim his desire, he will begin moving toward it. In so doing, he will begin his unwitting slide away from the Truth and into the grasp of the Lie. The closer he gets to the Thing He Wants, the more he will blindly pursue it, until it becomes an obsession, beyond the bounds of reason or logic and even beyond his own previous ethics.

(For more information about the Thing Your Character Wants, see Chapters 2 and 18 in *Creating Character Arcs*.)

Write down four possible Things Your Character Wants. These are deep primal desires. They are *not* necessarily your character's story goal, but they will influence the specific goal.

EXAMPLES:

- Prevent anyone from endangering those he loves.
  (*Star Wars*)

- Protect his family.
  (*The Godfather*)

Desire #1: _____

_____

_____.

Desire #2: _____

_____

_____.

Desire #3: _____

_____

_____.

Desire #4: _____

_____

_____.

What specific story goal arises from each of these desires? This will be the plot goal your character will be working toward over the course of your entire story.

Examples:

- Gain power from the Force.
- Take over his Mob family's illegal business.

Goal Arising From Desire #1: _____

_____

_____.

Goal Arising From Desire #2: _____

_____

_____.

Goal Arising From Desire #3: _____

_____

_____.

Goal Arising From Desire #4: _____

_____

_____.

Which of these four desires will be the primary Thing Your Character Wants in this story? Which one best guides your plot and theme?

☐ Desire #1
☐ Desire #2
☐ Desire #3
☐ Desire #4

Final Choice of the Thing Your Character Wants: _____

_____

_____.

Which of the four goals will be your character's primary plot goal in this story? Which one best represents the Thing He Wants and drives your plot?

☐ Goal #1
☐ Goal #2
☐ Goal #3
☐ Goal #4

Final Choice of Character's Plot Goal: _____

_____

_____

_____

_____.

THE NORMAL WORLD

JUST AS IN the Flat Arc, the Normal World in which a Corruption-Arc story opens will represent the harmony and hope of the Truth. The character will start out in a comparatively wonderful Normal World, already blessed by the Truth. Despite whatever drawbacks it may also possess, it offers the character a comparatively safe place of happiness and growth.

(For more information about the Normal World in a Corruption Arc, see Chapter 18 in *Creating Character Arcs*.)

What Normal World setting will best set up your character's arc? _____

_____

_____.

Will this Normal World be destroyed or endangered at the First Plot Point,

or will the protagonist choose to journey away from it to seek new opportuni-

ties? How will this occur? _____

_____

_____.

How is the Truth reflected in your character's exterior world and/or how can the

exterior world be a metaphor for the Truth your protagonist ends up rejecting? _____

_____

_____

_____.

- On its exterior, Anakin's Normal World as greedy Watto's slave on Ta-tooine is less than great. But his skills as a mechanic and pilot mean he and his mother are treated well. They live happily together, content in each other's love.
(*Star Wars*)

- Michael's Normal World is that of a smart and upright man who is moving away from his corrupt family into a promising new and legal life of his own, with his non-Italian girlfriend Kay being the clear symbol of the life he desires.
(*The Godfather*)

How will the Normal World visibly prove to readers (*show* them) the protagonist's "before" state at the beginning of the story? _____

_____

_____

_____.

What setting for the Normal World provides the most logical backstory for your character's Ghost? _____

_____

_____.

Why has your protagonist never chosen to leave the Normal World before now? ____

_____

_____

_____.

How will the Normal World contrast with the Adventure World that will follow in

the next two acts? _____

_____

_____

_____

_____

_____.

The Characteristic Moment

AS IN THE other arcs, the primary function of a Corruption Arc's Characteristic Moment is to introduce the character's true self. This encompasses more than just the character's personality and focus (both of which are important); it also needs to hint at the character's *potential*, specifically as it pertains to his relationship with the Lie. Even if the character starts out as a perfectly likable chap who helps little old ladies across the street, readers still need to gain an almost immediate sense of the dark nature that will lead to his doomed future.

(For more information on the Characteristic Moment in a Corruption Arc, see chapter 18 in *Creating Character Arcs*.)

Before you can craft the perfect Characteristic Moment, you must first know something about your character. Answer the following questions for starters (and for a full character interview, see my books *Outlining Your Novel* and the *Outlining Your Novel Workbook*).

What is this character's role in the story?

☐ Protagonist

☐ Antagonist

☐ Mentor

☐ Sidekick

☐ Love Interest

☐ Other: _____

What is your character's name? _____.

How old is your character? _____.

Of what nationality is your character? _____.

What is your character's occupation or primary identity (e.g., stay-at-home mom, rebel soldier)? _____

_____.

Does the character have any important physical characteristics (e.g., a limp, green

scales)? _____

_____

_____.

Name three prevailing aspects of the character's personality (e.g., kindness, quick temper, wit):

1. _____.

2. _____.

3. _____.

What *one* important personality trait, virtue, or skill best sums up your character?

_____

_____

_____.

How can you dramatize this aspect of your character to its fullest extent? ____

_____

_____.

How can you dramatize this aspect in a way that also introduces the plot? ____

_____

_____.

What do you want readers to find most sympathetic and/or interesting about this character? _____

_____.

How can you dramatize this aspect of your character in an opening scene? __

_____

_____.

What is your character's overall story goal and/or the Thing He Wants Mosts? ___

_____

_____.

How can you set up this goal or show the coming need for it in an opening

scene? _____

_____.

What is your character's scene goal in the opening chapter? _____

_____

_____.

How will you dramatize this scene goal right from the start of your opening

scene? _____

_____.

How will the character's pursuit of this goal meet with an obvious obstacle (i.e., conflict)? _____

_____

_____.

How will this goal move the plot, either by immediately causing consequences or setting them up for later? _____

_____

_____.

In your first chapter, how can you dramatize the contrast between the exterior Truth your character embraces and the seeds of the Lie already present within him? _____

_____

_____.

What is your character's scene goal in the opening chapter? _____

_____

_____.

How will you dramatize this scene goal right from the start of your opening scene? _____

_____.

How will the character's pursuit of this goal meet with an obvious obstacle (i.e., conflict)? _____

_____

_____.

How will this goal move the plot, either by immediately causing consequences or setting them up for later? _____

_____

_____.

How can any of the above help you demonstrate, or at least hint at, your character's Truth? _____

_____.

If appropriate, how can you reveal or at least hint at your character's Ghost? _____

_____

_____.

How can any of the above help you demonstrate, or at least hint at, your character's Lie? _____

_____

_____.

How can you craft the above elements to make your protagonist immediately appealing to readers (e.g., what's keeping them from looking away?)?_____

_____

_____

_____.

Which of your character's strengths can you show readers right away? _____

_____

_____.

Which of your character's pertinent weaknesses (especially Lie-driven weaknesses) can you show readers right away? _____

_____.

List events or activities you can use in your opening chapter to dramatize all the of above. Try to think of "big" moments that are unique, visually engaging, and keep the characters in motion.

1. _____.

2. _____.

3. _____.

4. _____.

5. _____.

Write a summary of your opening chapter and how you will introduce your character in a memorable and engaging Characteristic Moment: _____

_____

_____

_____

_____

_____

_____

_____

_____

_____

_____

_____

_____

_____.

Which of the following does your proposed Characteristic Moment accomplish?

- ☐ Introduce character.
- ☐ Reveal character's name.
- ☐ Indicate character's gender.
- ☐ Indicate character's age group.
- ☐ Indicate character's nationality.
- ☐ Indicate character's occupation/main identity.
- ☐ Indicate any important physical characteristics.
- ☐ Indicate role in the story (i.e., protagonist).
- ☐ Demonstrate prevailing aspect of personality.
- ☐ Hook readers' sympathy and/or interest.
- ☐ Demonstrate scene goal.
- ☐ Indicate story goal.
- ☐ Demonstrate (or at least hint at) Lie.
- ☐ Move plot directly or through foreshadowing.

If you're unable to combine the majority of the above elements into one scene, answer whether it would work better to divide the necessary characteristic elements into two or more scenes.

_____

_____

_____

_____

_____

_____.

THE FIRST ACT

From the 1% mark to the 25% mark in your story.

AS IN ANY type of character arc, the Corruption Arc's First Act must be spent developing both the Truth and the Lie. Whenever either the Truth or the Lie is on stage, the other is there as well, if only by reflection. Even though the Corruption-Arc character starts out understanding the Truth, readers still need to understand how the Lie has shaped the protagonist's world and how he relates to it personally.

Just as importantly, you must establish the stakes. What is at stake for everyone in the story if the protagonist pursues the Lie? What must he sacrifice if he chooses the Truth over the Lie? Don't make the choices too black and white. Whenever a character makes an important decision, it should be a difficult one. Whatever he chooses, he will have to sacrifice something of great value. Likewise, whatever he chooses, he will also gain something of great value.

The character won't yet have the insight necessary to name either the Truth or the Lie. He has no idea he's dealing with anything so grand. All he knows is that he's being presented with choices. Something in his life isn't quite right, and he wants to make it better, one way or the other. His first major decision and action—which will force him out of his Normal World—won't happen until the end of the First Act. Up until that point, spend your time upping the ante on his personal discomfort and leading him to the opportunities that will set his feet on the path away from the Truth.

(For more information about the First Act in a Corruption Arc, see Chapter 18 in *Creating Character Arcs*.)

How can you demonstrate what is at stake for the protagonist to lose if she were to

succumb to the Lie? _____

_____

_____

_____.

Is the character immediately cognizant of the Lie's temptation?

☐ Yes

☐ No

If not, how will he grow into an awareness of its apparent benefits and the possibility of pursuing it over the course of the First Act? _____

_____

_____.

If the character is aware of the Lie, why has he been able to resist engaging with it up to this point? _____

_____.

Name three ways you will continue to reinforce the world's Lie or introduce more of its facets throughout the First Act:

1. _____.

2. _____.

3. _____.

What specific weakness makes your protagonist susceptible to the Lie? _____

_____.

Even if this trait isn't yet fully developed, how can you hint right from the beginning that the seed is there? _____

_____.

What Inciting Event will be the Call to Adventure that first brushes your character

against the main conflict? _____

_____

_____

_____.

EXAMPLE:

- Anakin meets the Jedi Knight Qui-Gon, which stirs his own latent desires to escape slavery, gain power, and return to rescue his mother. (*Star Wars*)

- Michael learns an assassination attempt has been made on his father's life, leaving him fighting for his life in a hospital. This causess Michael's family feeling and loyalty to draw him back toward the criminal underworld. (*The Godfather*)

How will this Inciting Event set up the character's entry into the Adventure World

of the main conflict in the Second Act? _____

_____

_____.

Does the Inciting Event initially seem:

    ☐ a good thing.

    ☐ a bad thing.

How will the Call to Adventure initially be met with resistance or refusal? _____

_____

_____.

Will the protagonist be the one to initially reject the Call to Adventure, or will someone else try to reject it for him? _____.

How long will it take the protagonist to stop resisting?
    ☐ Entire rest of the First Act up to the First Plot Point.
    ☐ Shorter period ending with what event _____.

How does the Inciting Event change the protagonist's awareness of and attraction to the Lie, in however small or subconscious a way? _____

_____

_____.

What will the protagonist decide to *do* about the Call to Adventure at the Inciting Event? _____

_____

_____.

EXAMPLE:

- After Qui-Gon wins Anakin's freedom from Watto in a bet, Anakin makes the decision to follow his heart, leave his mother, and go with Qui-Gon to Coruscant to become a Jedi.

- Michael immediately rushes to his family, bribing a crooked cop to help him protect his father from another attempt on his life.

THE FIRST PLOT POINT

WHERE DOES IT BELONG?

25% of the way into your story.

THE FIRST PLOT Point shifts your protagonist out of the safe Normal World of his Truth and into an uncertain new Adventure World. At this point, he likely has only good and pure goals. Like the Disillusionment Arc character, he is idealistic and, insofar as he is aware of the Lie, doesn't yet have any real understanding of its dark potential.

(For more information about the First Plot Point in a Corruption Arc, see Chapter 19 in *Creating Character Arcs*.)

What event occurs at the end of the First Act that causes your character to leave

the Normal World and irreversibly engage with the main conflict? _____

_____

_____

_____.

EXAMPLE:

- After Qui-Gon is murdered by the Sith Lord Darth Maul, the Jedi Council grudgingly accepts Anakin as Obi-Wan Kenobi's new apprentice. Anakin moves from his Normal World of a backwater slave child to that of an elite Jedi Padawan living on the opulent planet Coruscant.
  (*Star Wars*)

- Michael sets up a meeting with the rival mobster and dirty cop responsible for shooting his father. Even though he is racked by nerves, he murders both men—irrevocably plunging him into the world of his family's business, which he has striven to stay clear of up to now.
  (*The Godfather*)

In what way might this event be surprising even after the Inciting Event? _____

_____

_____

_____.

Which of the following best describes your First Plot Point?

☐   A seemingly positive opportunity.

EXAMPLE:

- Anakin is given the opportunity to better himself by becoming a Jedi.

☐   Something disastrous.

EXAMPLE:

- Michael Corleone commits murder in his family's defense.

What decision on your character's part led him right up to the First Plot Point,

making him at least partially responsible for what happens? _____

_____

_____

_____.

EXAMPLE:

- Anakin actively desired and chose to be a Jedi Padawan, even under-standing the limitations (i.e., he must submit to the Order's authority and never form an attachment outside of it).

- Michael independently makes the choice to kill his father's would-be murderers, even though he could have allowed them to go free or to have a member of his father's criminal organization commit the deed instead.

Which of the following best describes your First Plot Point?

- ☐ It destroys the Normal World, leaving the protagonist no choice but to move on.
- ☐ It physically removes the protagonist from the Normal World.
- ☐ It warps the Normal World, forcing the protagonist to adapt to new ways of surviving within it.

Which best describes your protagonist's reaction to the First Plot Point?

- ☐ Enthusiasm—she wants to enter the conflict of the Second Act.
- ☐ Resistance—she must be forced to enter the conflict of the Second Act.

How will the First Plot Point force your character into a reaction that directly pits his taken-for-granted Truth against his subconscious Lie? _____

_____

_____

_____

_____.

Why do the events of the First Plot Point lead him to believe his First-Act tactics (of always using the Truth as his go-to method) will no longer be as successful? _____

_____

_____

_____.

What definitive action will he take to move forward into the Adventure World of the main conflict? _____

_____

_____.

Name three new physical needs that must be met in the aftermath of the First Plot Point:

1. _____.

2. _____.

3. _____.

What definitive new plot goal will the character now pursue?_____

_____

_____

_____.

Example:

- Anakin's new plot goal is to become a powerful Jedi, so he can protect those he loves.
- Michael's new goal is to find his feet and survive in the dangerous new crime world he has plunged himself into.

  Do you want the character to ultimately achieve this goal?

☐ Yes.
   Why? _____.

☐ No.
   Why? _____.

THE FIRST HALF OF THE SECOND ACT

WHERE DOES IT BELONG?

From the 25% mark to the 50% mark in your story.

THE SECOND ACT in a Negative Change Arc bears a lot of similarity to that in a Positive Change Arc. In both types of arc, the character will be thrust out of his Normal World into a new and strange dilemma, where he will be forced to confront his Lie. He'll be learning more about that Lie and be given opportunities to recognize its latent power over him.

Here, however, the character becomes increasingly enthralled by the darkness, rather than overcoming it. The character is going to be learning more and more about the power of the Lie. He recognizes it, if only subconsciously, as a path toward the Thing He Wants. As his obsession with the Thing He Wants increases, he begins more and more to embrace the Lie and reject the Truth.

(For more information about the First Half of the Second Act in a Corruption Arc, see Chapter 19 in *Creating Character Arcs*.)

What catalyst (possibly in the form of information from another character) will your

protagonist begin to receive that tempts her into believing the Lie is a good and help-

ful thing? _____

_____.

EXAMPLE:

- A now-grown Anakin begins to form a relationship with Chancellor Palpatine, who cleverly begins poisoning Anakin's Truth by suggesting exploitative power should be Anakin's true end goal.
(*Star Wars*)

- While hiding out in Sicily, Michael marries an Italian girl, symbolically rejecting the upright and normal life he could have led with Kay, and instead binding himself to the notorious Sicilian way.
(*The Godfather*)

How can other characters remind your protagonist of the Truth by demonstrating

it, rather than just *telling* her about it? _____

_____

_____.

How is your protagonist feeling slightly out of place within the new Adventure World

of the Second Act? _____

_____.

What Truth-based belief is the protagonist still trying to use to reach his goals? ____

_____

_____.

How is the character's increasing half-heartedness about the Truth holding him

back from being truly effective? _____

_____.

EXAMPLE:

- Anakin is passionate about being a Jedi and the power it allows him to wield, but he also resents the rules the Jedi Order enforces in his life. He rebels against them and pursues a forbidden romance with Senator Padmé Amidala, hoping he can hold onto both the Thing He Wants and the Thing He Needs.

- Michael goes on the run in Sicily, hiding from his family's enemies in the States. Although it's obvious he will never be able to return to the life he formerly desires, he still has not completely committed himself to the life of a mobster. He is caught between worlds—between the old Truth and the new Lie.

How is the protagonist demonstrating confusion or frustration about why the Truth isn't serving him as well as he thinks it should? _____

_____

_____.

How is the character experiencing increasing cognitive dissonance as he becomes more and more convinced of the worthwhile effectiveness of the Lie?

_____

_____.

What first move will he make to slowly begin evolving his tactics to incorporate the Lie? _____

_____.

How is the character pursuing the Thing She Wants in the Second Act? _____

_____

_____.

How is she failing to achieve her plot goal, thanks to her half-hearted embrace of the Truth? _____

_____

_____.

How is her pursuit of the Thing She Wants pushing her away from the Thing She

Needs? _____

_____

_____

_____

_____.

If the character continues down this path unchecked, what personal, spiritual,

and perhaps even physical destruction will she end up running into? _____

_____

_____

_____

_____.

Example:

- Anakin's mentors and friends warn him at every turn that pursuing unchecked power can only lead him to the Dark Side.
- If Michael embraces the darkness of his family's lifestyle, it is clear he will not live it halfheartedly, but embrace it to the full extent of its necessity.

THE MIDPOINT

WHERE DOES IT BELONG?

50% of the way into your story.

A S IN ANY type of arc, the character will encounter a Moment of Truth at the Midpoint. This is a startling revelation that clarifies the external conflict, while also giving the character the opportunity to see both the Truth and the Lie for what they really are.

Unlike a Positive Change Arc, however, the Corruption Arc will show the character hypnotized by the Lie. His fascination with it and subconscious belief that it is truly the best means to his end, whatever its drawbacks, finally overpowers him. He doesn't yet consciously reject the Truth, but from this point on, he is firmly in the Lie's thrall.

(For more information about the Midpoint in a Corruption Arc, see Chapter 19 in *Creating Character Arcs*.)

What is your story's Midpoint event? _____

_____

_____.

EXAMPLES:

- Anakin secretly rebels against everything the Jedi Order has commanded him and abandons his mission of protecting Padmé in order to fly back to Tatooine to try to rescue his mother from captivity and torture. When she dies in his arms, he surrenders to the power of the Dark Side for the first time and ruthlessly slaughters the entire Sand People village.
(*Star Wars*)

- When Michael's brother Sonny is killed, he returns home to take over the leadership of his family. He moves from a reactionary role, in the wake of committing murder to avenge his father, to fully embracing the active role of his new destiny.
(*The Godfather*)

What can you do to make this centerpiece scene as "big" as possible? _____

_____

_____

_____.

How have the events of the First Half of the Second Act led up to the Midpoint by

drawing your protagonist away from the hope represented by the Truth? _____

_____

_____

_____.

How will the external events of the Midpoint prompt a "Moment of Truth," in

which the character sees the benefits of the Truth but cannot bring himself to em

brace it? _____

_____

_____.

What worse manifestation of his Lie will he embrace instead? _____

_____

_____

_____.

EXAMPLE:

- Just prior to the Midpoint, Anakin argues for a secret relationship with Padmé in defiance of his vows to the Jedi, but Padmé resists, insisting she couldn't live a lie. In that instance, Anakin experiences a Moment of Truth, in which he recognizes the correctness of her words ("You're right. It would destroy us.") and struggles to acquiesce to them. But he ultimately rejects them and marries her anyway.

- Michael becomes an even more ruthless Mafia lord than was his own father, brooking no resistance from those who have tried or would try again to harm his family or anyone connected to them.

How will the events of the Midpoint act as a swivel between the two halves of your story—shifting your character out of uninformed reaction and into educated action in the external plot? _____

_____

_____.

In the second half of the story, how will the character use his new embrace of the Lie to force his way toward the Thing He Wants—but in an obsessive and destructive manner? _____

_____.

Even as he makes progress toward his plot goal, how will the character continue to be "punished" for his Lie-based actions in a way that prevents him from achieving total victory while still in the Second Act? _____

_____.

THE SECOND HALF OF THE SECOND ACT

WHERE DOES IT BELONG?

From the 50% mark to the 75% mark in your story.

AFTER HIS REVELATION and rejection of the Truth at the Midpoint, the character will now begin actively and aggressively pursuing the Thing He Wants in the Second Half of the Second Act. Although he will still experience glimmers of the Truth (particularly in the form of resistance and reprimands from supporting characters), he has already all but cast off its fetters. The Truth is no longer a personal obstacle between him and his Lie-driven goal.

(For more information about the Second Half of the Second Act in a Corruption Arc, see Chapter 19 in *Creating Character Arcs*.)

How is the character acting on the Lie she embraced at the Midpoint? _____

_____

_____

_____

_____.

What new (but destructive) "tools" did the Lie provide your character that are allow-

ing him to make better progress toward the Thing He Wants? _____

_____

_____

_____.

What obstacles will the antagonistic force still be putting in his way? _____

_____

_____

_____.

EXAMPLE:

- Throughout the Second Half of the Second Act, Anakin consistently and obsessively chooses to protect Padmé over any and all practical or moral restraints—losing an arm and nearly sacrificing his master in the process. He secretly marries her in defiance of his vows and, as time goes by, proves himself willing to seek answers even from the Dark Side in order to save her from dying in childbirth. (*Star Wars*)

- Michael goes to Las Vegas and begins consolidating power for himself and his family in their war against the Five Families. (*The Godfather*)

How is the Truth still present in the character's life, if only on a subconscious level?

_____

_____.

Name four destructive consequences the character's Lie-driven mindset and actions are having on the world and characters around him:

1. _____.

2. _____.

3. _____.

4. _____.

Name the destructive consequences the character's Lie-driven mindset and actions are having on himself:

Mentally: _____.

Emotionally: _____.

Physically: _____.

Spiritually: _____.

How is the character in more desperate need than ever of the Thing She Needs—

even though she won't admit it? _____

_____.

Write down four scenes from the first half of the story in which your character demonstrated the Truth at work in his life. Then brainstorm four scenes you can include in the second half that will contrast the earlier scenes by showing how your character's Lie has already started to change him.

"Before" Scenes   **"After" Scenes**

1._____   1._____

2._____   2._____

3._____   3._____

4._____   4._____

EXAMPLE:

- **Before:** Anakin was a loving and generous child who treated others with respect and kindness.
- **After:** As Anakin succumbs more and more to his Lie, he becomes moody, angry, and prideful and begins alienating even the loved ones he is selling his soul to protect.

At the end of the Second Act, how will the Thing the Character Wants place itself within the character's grasp, offering a seeming victory? _____

_____

_____

_____.

EXAMPLE:

- Anakin learns from Palpatine that the Dark Side may have the answers to saving Padmé from death.
- Michael promises his second wife (and original girlfriend) Kay that he will legitimize the family business. He is still masquerading his new life under the old pretense that he can avoid being drawn into the realities of the Mafia.

How must the character utterly subject himself to the Lie in order to claim the Thing He Wants? _____

_____

_____

_____.

How will the character entirely sacrifice the Thing He Needs in order to gain the Thing He Wants at this point? _____

_____

_____

_____.

How does the character justify this to himself? _____

_____

_____

_____

_____.

THE THIRD PLOT POINT

WHERE DOES IT BELONG?

75% of the way into your story.

JUST AS IN the Fall Arc, the Third Plot Point in the Corruption Arc brings the character not to his greatest defeat yet—but to his greatest triumph. Or so it seems. His Lie seems to put the Thing He Wants within his grasp, and he seizes it—but at a cost greater than even he could have imagined. In essence, this victory *is* a defeat. The character has sold his soul to gain his goal, and for the entire rest of the story, he must reap the consequences.

The previous two acts have been all about the setup for this inevitable destruction. The character has been making active choices, but since they've all been based on the false foundation of the Lie, they've turned out to be horribly wrong choices. Unlike Positive Change Arc characters, who will make mistakes but will then recognize and learn from those mistakes, the Negative Change Arc character will refuse to even recognize his mistakes, much less embrace opportunities to grow past them and rectify them.

(For more information about the Third Plot Point in a Corruption Arc, see Chapter 20 in *Creating Character Arcs*.)

What Third Plot Point crisis will bring your protagonist to an exterior victory that

wreaks havoc on the world and characters around him? _____

_____

_____

_____

_____

_____.

EXAMPLE:

- Anakin realizes he cannot allow Mace Windu and the other Jedi Masters to kill the Sith Lord Darth Sidious. His desperate need to protect his wife, no matter the cost, prompts him to save the life of the man who has already killed millions and will kill millions more. More than that, he surrenders himself as an apprentice to the Dark Side, in order to learn Sidious's secrets of life and death.
(*Star Wars*)

- Michael's father dies, raising Michael to full and final headship of his family. He is king: he is victorious. But he is a criminal: he has sacrificed the Truth.
(*The Godfather*)

How do other characters react to what the protagonist does at the Third Plot Point?

_____

_____

_____.

How will some of your supporting characters demonstrate the better road the

protagonist might have walked had he chosen the Truth here? _____

_____

_____.

How will other supporting characters demonstrate their own negative descent

as a result of the protagonist's influence? _____

_____

_____.

How does the Third Plot Point definitively prove the protagonist's choice between the Thing She Wants and the Thing She Needs by forcing her to sacrifice the latter?

_____

_____.

How can you make the character's rejection of the Truth as painful as possible? _____

_____.

How can you contrast the healing power of the Truth with the greater temptation of the victory the Lie promises at this point? _____

_____

_____

_____.

How can you cast the pall of death over the Third Plot Point by featuring it either literally or symbolically? _____

_____

_____.

EXAMPLE:

- In addition to the all-important threat of Padmé's death in childbirth, Anakin and Palpatine murder Mace Windu and other Jedi Masters.
- Michael's father dies.

The First Half of the Third Act

Where Does It Belong?

From the 75% mark to the 88% mark in your story.

WITHOUT THE TRUTH, the protagonist has no tools with which to cope with the tragic events of the Third Plot Point. As a result, he spends the first half of the Third Act (prior to the Climax) determined to strike out at the antagonistic force and reach for the Thing He Wants *any way he can*. He will commit any number of crimes and sins. He has nothing left to lose and no moral compass to guide him. Supporting characters may try to reason with him, but he will now be even less open to their suggestions than he was previously. He may even turn on people whom he was previously willing to accept despite their differing opinions.

(For more information about the First Half of the Third Act in a Fall Arc, see Chapter 20 in *Creating Character Arcs*.)

How can you up the stakes after the Third Plot Point by emphasizing the emptiness

of your protagonist's victory? _____

_____.

Will the character have reason to at least momentarily regret his decision to abandon

the Truth? _____

_____.

How will your character try to block his pain with the conviction that he made the

only possible choice and that the Thing He Wants is worth the price? _____

_____.

EXAMPLE:

- Believing the Dark Side is the only possible solution to saving his wife, Anakin throws himself into the darkness completely. Even as he mourns the atrocities his new master orders him to commit, he doesn't flinch from them. He can't afford to. He's come too far. The hole is too deep, and there's no way back up. His only chance for himself and his wife is to dig deeper still. After Mace Windu's death, Anakin slaughters the Jedi, young and old alike, as well as the Separatist Coalition—and anyone else who gets in his and his new master's way.
(*Star Wars*)

- Michael is now fully committed to his new lifestyle. He has internally come to peace with it, even as it demands greater and greater sacrifices of morality.
(*The Godfather*)

Even after your character fully claims the Lie, how can you keep your character off-balance by forcing him to look at how life would have been better with the Truth? _

_____

_____

_____

_____.

Name four ways it is becoming increasingly difficult for the character to maintain sanity and centeredness amidst the consequences and continuing progress of his Lie:

1. _____.

2. _____.

3. _____.

4. _____.

How is your character different in the Third Act from who he was in the First Act? _

_____

_____

_____.

How can you demonstrate this by giving your protagonist the opportunity to symbolically reject the wholeness offered by the Truth in a physical way? ____

_____

_____.

EXAMPLE:

- Realizing what Anakin is doing, a heartbroken Padmé begs him to give up the Dark Side and run away with her, where Palpatine cannot influence him. Anakin not only refuses, but in his growing rage, lashes out at her, nearly killing the very person he has been trying to save.

- No longer the boyish war hero, Michael has fully adopted the mantle of his family's leader, in the wake of his father's death.

Prior to the Climax, how can you use a minor character to try to convince the protagonist to finally abandon the Lie? _____

_____

_____.

EXAMPLE:

- Obi-Wan tracks Anakin down and tries to convince him of the error of his ways.

THE CLIMAX
WHERE DOES IT BELONG?

From the 88% mark to the 98% mark in your story.

THE CLIMAX IS where everything finally and fully falls apart. The character's last desperate push to use the Lie to gain the Thing He Wants will achieve one of two possible outcomes:

1. He gains an apparent outer victory, in which he is able to claim the Thing He Wants, but in which his success is a hollow one. Without the Truth, he can never find inner wholeness by gaining the Thing He Needs. In this type of ending, the Climactic Moment will likely include a glimpse of the Truth, in which the character comes to the crushing realization that his battle was a wasteful one and, worse, that the outrages he's committed along the way have destroyed both himself and everything he once loved.

2. He loses both the inner and the outer battle. His inability to equip himself with the Truth dooms him to failure in his final conflict.

(For more information about the Climax in a Corruption Arc, see Chapter 20 in *Creating Character Arcs*.)

What one moment have readers been waiting for since the beginning of the story? _
_____.

How can you deliver this moment? _____

_____.

How has your character recently proven *before* the Climax that she will do anything

she must to reach her goal? _____

_____

_____.

What form will the final confrontation between the protagonist and the antagonistic

force take? _____

_____.

EXAMPLES:

- Naval battle.
  (*Master and Commander*)

- Horse race.
  (*The Reivers by William Faulkner*)

- Filibuster.
  (*Mr. Smith Goes to Washington*)

Where will your Climax take place? _____.

How does this setting symbolically emphasize the central conflict and the

theme? _____.

How does this setting physically or emotionally make the confrontation with

the antagonist more difficult? _____

_____.

How is the nature of the final climactic confrontation perfectly suited to provide the

final test for your protagonist's new Lie, absolutely proving her devotion to it? _____

_____

_____

_____.

How will the antagonistic force attempt to use the Truth to change the protagonist's mind one last time—and fail? _____

_____

_____.

How will the protagonist attempt to use her new Lie to overcome the antagonistic force and remove the last obstacle between herself and her main plot goal? _____

_____

_____.

Do you want the protagonist to achieve his plot goal and gain the Thing He Wants?

Why? _____

_____

_____.

If the protagonist fails in reaching his goal, how will he react to his utter defeat? _____

_____

_____.

If the protagonist succeeds in reaching his goal, how will he react to its comparative emptiness? _____

_____

_____.

Will your protagonist die in the Climactic Moment?

☐ Yes

☐ No

How will your Climactic Moment emphasize, either blatantly or ironically, the utter futility of the character's Lie? _____

_____

_____

_____.

EXAMPLE:

- After dealing his beloved wife a death blow, Anakin turns on Obi-Wan and is eventually brutally wounded as a result of his blind faith in his own power.
  (*Star Wars*)

THE RESOLUTION
WHERE DOES IT BELONG?

From the 98% mark to the 100% mark in your story.

SOME SMALL POSTSCRIPT is almost always necessary at the end of a Negative Change Arc. In the event of your protagonist's death, you'll need to show the surviving characters' reactions, especially since many of them will probably have undergone Disillusionment Arcs as a result of witnessing his fall. You'll want to show the effect of the protagonist's actions upon the world around him. Presumably, he's left it a worse place than that in which it started, but you may want to hint at the possibility for new hope now that the protagonist's dark influence has been lifted.

(For more information about the Resolution in a Corruption Arc, see Chapter 20 in *Creating Character Arcs*.)

Now that the plot goal has proved itself utterly unworthy of the sacrifices the protagonist made, how is she able to face the future? _____

_____.

How will the available choices for her new life moving forward contrast with the choices she was offered back in the first chapter? _____

_____

_____.

If your protagonist died in the Climax, how can you indicate what will happen to the surviving characters moving forward? _____

_____.

Name three ways you can contrast the Normal World from the beginning of the story with the new normal.

1. _____.

2. _____.

3. _____.

If it is possible for you to *physically* return your characters to the Normal World,

how can you contrast their new selves with the old world? _____

_____

_____

_____.

How will your Resolution answer the Thematic Question you asked in the first chapter?

_____

_____.

EXAMPLE:

- **Thematic Question:** Can love be forcibly preserved and protected?
- **Thematic Answer:** No, love only exists when it is surrendered.

How can you visually *show* the consequences of the character's Lie without slap-

ping readers in the face with the "moral of the story"? _____

_____

_____.

EXAMPLE:

- After Anakin is maimed in battle, his wife dies in childbirth, just as he feared—not in spite of his attempts to save her, but because of them. (*Star Wars*)

- When Michael's wife demands to know if he's committed the recent string of brutal murders, designed to end the Mob war, he denies it—only to explicitly demonstrate the truth when he allows others to call him "Don Corleone" and close the door, symbolically, on the upright life he might once have made with his wife. (*The Godfather*)

Do you wish to end the story on a downbeat note emphasizing the horror of the Lie, or an upbeat note indicating the latent restorative power of the Truth? _____

_____

_____.

EXAMPLE:

- Anakin is rescued from death by his new master and confined to life as a monstrous cyborg. His story, however, ends with the promise of "a new hope" in the galaxy, via his newborn children.

- Michael has become a far greater monster than his father ever was, unmitigated in the brutalities he is willing to commit, even down to murdering his brother-in-law on the very day he becomes his nephew's godfather. He is victorious, but he has clearly sacrificed his soul.

CREATIVE EXERCISE:

Consider the reasons your character was not strong enough in his initial Truth to resist the call of the Lie.

SOMETHING TO THINK ABOUT:

1. Even though the character's Normal World is nourished by the Truth, why is the character still less than comfortable in this world?
2. How can you use the Characteristic Moment to introduce your character's proclivity toward the Lie?
3. At the Midpoint, what Moment of Truth gives your character an opportunity to embrace the Truth? Why and how does he reject it?
4. Why does your character's refusal to embrace the Truth render him powerless to rise from the Third Plot Point better equipped to deal with both his inner and outer conflict?

RESOURCES:

- "What's the Difference Between Your Story's Theme and Its Message?," helpingwritersbecomeauthors.com/storys-theme-2
- "Why You Should Write More Than One Ending to Your Book," helpingwritersbecomeauthors.com/write-one-ending-book
- "3 Tips for How to Write a Bad Guy Who Transforms Your Story," helpingwritersbecomeauthors.com/why-devil-makes-boring-bad-guy
- "Planning Your Story: What George Lucas Can Teach You (Not) to Do," helpingwritersbecomeauthors.com/planning-your-story
- "Your Fiction May Be Failing for One Simple Reason: You're Not Being Honest," helpingwritersbecomeauthors.com/your-fiction-may-be-failing-for-one-simple-reason-youre-not-being-honest

CONCLUSION

JANE EYRE CHANGED my life.

I read Charlotte Brontë's classic novel for the first time as a fourteen-year-old and, frankly, struggled with its lengthy First and Third Acts and its aggressively self-observant protagonist. I never thought I'd return to it. But when I was asked to begin work on an annotated version of the book for *Writer's Digest*, I came back for a second look.

What I found blew my mind, revolutionized my awareness of story theory, and broadened my mind to a finer understanding of the world and my experience within it. What I found, of course, were character arcs.

It was in studying and annotating Jane Eyre's near-flawless approach to the Positive Change Arc that the specifics of character arc clicked for me.

The Lie the Character Believes juxtaposed against a greater Truth.

The conflict between the Thing the Character Wants and the Thing the Character Needs.

The perfect harmony of character evolution within the established beats of story structure.

All of these revelations, and more, forever changed the way I looked at story. In the years since, my own stories have grown richer, deeper, and, perhaps not so surprisingly, easier and more exciting to write.

What is perhaps a little more surprising is that my life has changed too. Identifying the arc of character within story theory not only helped me create better books, it also helped me understand the cycles I live through in my own life. Like my characters, I stubbornly hold onto damaging Lies and am compelled into journeys of reaction and action as I live out all five of the arcs (with varying levels of drama) in my own life.

From this arises a beautiful circle: my life teaches me how to write better stories, and my stories teach me how to live a better life.

If you can take nothing more away from our exploration of character arcs, I hope you are able to accept that one precious gift.

Happy writing!
K.M. Weiland

Note From K.M. Weiland: Thanks so much for reading! I hope you've enjoyed learning how to write powerful and effective character arcs. Did you know that reviews are what sell books? If the Creating Character Arcs Workbook was helpful to you, would you consider rating and reviewing it? Thank you and happy writing!

Want more writing tips?

CLAIM YOUR FREE BOOK!

Featuring some of K.M. Weiland's most popular tips on character crafting, this book offers a firm foundation for understanding the basics of character building, as well as solid tips for troubleshooting.

Discover inspiring quotes from successful authors, writing prompts, and creativity exercises. This book gives you the tools you need to tackle your latest batch of charcters.

"Exactly the information and inspiration I was looking for to liven up my characters."

kmweiland.com/free-characters-book

ABOUT THE AUTHOR

K.M. WEILAND LIVES in make-believe worlds, talks to imaginary friends, and survives primarily on chocolate truffles and espresso. She is the IPPY, NIEA, and Lyra Award-winning and internationally published author of the popular writing guides Outlining Your Novel and Structuring Your Novel, as well as Jane Eyre: The Writer's Digest Annotated Classic, the dieselpunk adventure Storming, the medieval epic Behold the Dawn, and the portal fantasy Dreamlander. When she's not making things up, she's busy mentoring other authors through her award-winning blog Helping Writers Become Authors. She makes her home in western Nebraska. Visit her on Facebook or Twitter to participate in her Writing Question of the Day (#WQOTD). You can email her at kmweiland@kmweiland.com.

MORE WORKBOOKS FROM K.M. WEILAND

LEARN HOW TO MAKE YOUR FIRST DRAFT EASY!

- Create your own personalized outlining process
- Brainstorm premise and plot ideas
- Discover your characters
- Choose and create the right settings
- Organize your scenes

DISCOVER THE PROVEN BLUEPRINT FOR CREATING STORIES THAT SELL

- Implement a strong three-act structure
- Time your acts and your plot points
- Unleash your unique and personal vision for your story
- Identify common structural weaknesses and flip them around into stunning strengths
- Eliminate saggy middles by discovering your story's "centerpiece"
- And so much more!

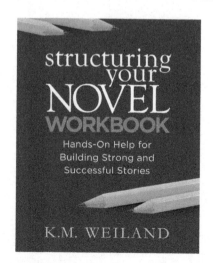

HelpingWritersBecomeAuthors.com

FURTHER

RESOURCES

The Urban Setting Thesaurus:
A Writer's Guide to City Spaces
by **Angela Ackerman & Becca Puglisi**

The key to creating stronger descriptions by showing writers how multi-sensory details can draw readers in and enhance the story.

writershelpingwriters.net/bookstore

Writing Fiction for All You're Worth:
Strategies and Techniques
for Taking Your Fiction to the Next Level
by **James Scott Bell**

The best of James Scott Bell's articles and blog posts on writing, easily searchable under these headings: The Writing World, The Writing Life, and The Writing Craft.

amzn.to/1xj86TF

Made in the USA
Las Vegas, NV
20 March 2021